Activity Book

EXPLORING THE UNIVERSE

Prentice Hall
Englewood Cliffs, New Jersey
Needham, Massachusetts

Activity Book

PRENTICE HALL SCIENCE
Exploring the Universe

ISBN 0-13-401159-7

        10   97 96

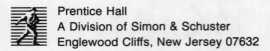
Prentice Hall
A Division of Simon & Schuster
Englewood Cliffs, New Jersey 07632

Contents

To the Teacher

The materials in the *Activity Book* are designed to assist you in teaching the *Prentice Hall Science* program. These materials will be especially helpful to you in accommodating a wide range of student ability levels. In particular, the activities have been designed to reinforce and extend a variety of science skills and to encourage critical thinking, problem solving, and discovery learning. The highly visual format of many activities heightens student interest and enthusiasm.

All the materials in the *Activity Book* have been developed to facilitate student comprehension of, and interest in, science. Pages intended for student use may be made into overhead transparencies and masters or used as photocopy originals. The reproducible format allows you to have these items easily available in the quantity you need. All appropriate answers to questions and activities are found at the end of each section in a convenient Answer Key.

CHAPTER MATERIALS

In order to stimulate and increase student interest, the *Activity Book* includes a wide variety of activities and worksheets. All the activities and worksheets are correlated to individual chapters in the student textbook.

Table of Contents

Each set of chapter materials begins with a Table of Contents that lists every component for the chapter and the page number on which it begins. The Table of Contents also lists the number of the page on which the Answer Key for the chapter activities and worksheets begins. In addition, the Table of Contents page for each chapter has a shaded bar running along the edge of the page. This shading will enable you to easily spot where a new set of chapter materials begins.

Whenever an activity might be considered a problem-solving or discovery-learning activity, it is so marked on the Contents page. In addition, each activity that can be used for cooperative-learning groups has an asterisk beside it on the Contents page.

First in the chapter materials is a Chapter Discovery. The Chapter Discovery is best used prior to students reading the chapter. It will enable students to discover for themselves some of the scientific concepts discussed within the chapter. Because of their highly visual design, simplicity, and hands-on approach to discovery learning, the Discovery Activities are particularly appropriate for ESL students in a cooperative-learning setting.

Chapter Activities

Chapter activities are especially visual, often asking students to draw conclusions from diagrams, graphs, tables, and other forms of data. Many chapter activities enable the student to employ problem-solving and critical-thinking skills. Others allow the student to utilize a discovery-learning approach to the topics covered in the chapter. In addition, most chapter activities are appropriate for cooperative-learning groups.

Laboratory Investigation Worksheet

Each chapter of the textbook contains a full-page Laboratory Investigation. A Laboratory Investigation worksheet in each set of chapter materials repeats the textbook Laboratory Investigation and provides formatted space for writing observations and conclusions. Students are aided by a formatted worksheet, and teachers can easily evaluate and grade students' results and progress. Answers to the Laboratory Investigation are provided in the Answer Key following the chapter materials, as well as in the Annotated Teacher's Edition of the textbook.

Answer Key

At the end of each set of chapter materials is an Answer Key for all activities and worksheets in the chapter.

SCIENCE READING SKILLS

Each textbook in *Prentice Hall Science* includes a special feature called the Science Gazette. Each gazette contains three articles.

The first article in every Science Gazette—called Adventures in Science— describes a particular discovery, innovation, or field of research of a scientist or group of scientists. Some of the scientists profiled in Adventures in Science are well known; others are not yet famous but have made significant contributions to the world of science. These articles provide students with firsthand knowledge about how scientists work and think, and give some insight into the scientists' personal lives as well.

Issues in Science is the second article in every gazette. This article provides a nonbiased description of a specific area of science in which various members of the scientific community or the population at large hold diverging opinions. Issues in Science articles introduce students to some of the "controversies" raging in science at the present time. While many of these issues are debated strictly in scientific terms, others involve social issues that pertain to science as well.

The third article in every Science Gazette is called Futures in Science. The setting of each Futures in Science article is some 15 to 150 years in the future and describes some of the advances people may encounter as science progresses through the years. However, these articles cannot be considered "science fiction," as they are all extrapolations of current scientific research.

The Science Gazette articles can be powerful motivators in developing an interest in science. However, they have been written with a second purpose in mind. These articles can be used as science readers. As such, they will both reinforce and enrich your students' ability to read scientific material. In order to better assess the science reading skills of your students, this *Activity Book* contains a variety of science reading activities based on the gazette articles. Each gazette article has an activity that can be distributed to students in order to evaluate their science reading skills.

There are a variety of science reading skills included in this *Activity Book*. These skills include Finding the Main Idea, Previewing, Critical Reading, Making Predictions, Outlining, Using Context Clues, and Making Inferences. These basic study skills are essential in understanding the content of all subject matter, and they can be particularly useful in the comprehension of science materials. Mastering such study skills can help students to study, learn new vocabulary terms, and understand information found in their textbooks.

ACTIVITY BANK

A special feature called the Activity Bank ends each textbook in *Prentice Hall Science*. The Activity Bank is a compilation of hands-on activities designed to reinforce and extend the science concepts developed in the textbook. Each activity that appears in the Activity Bank section of the textbook is reproduced here as a worksheet with space for recording observations and conclusions. Also included are additional activities in the form of worksheets. An Answer Key for all the activities is given. The Activity Bank activities provide opportunities to meet the diverse abilities and interests of students; to encourage problem solving, critical thinking, and discovery learning; to involve students more actively in the learning experience; and to address the need for ESL strategies and cooperative learning.

Contents

CHAPTER 1 ■ Stars and Galaxies

(**Note:** *This investigation is found on page M50 of the student textbook.*)

*Appropriate for cooperative learning

Chapter Discovery   **Stars and Galaxies**

The Big Bang

Background

Astronomers think the universe began in an enormous explosion called the big bang. Billions of years ago, all the matter and energy that now exist in the universe were concentrated into a hot, dense "primordial atom." Then, at the instant of the big bang, all this concentrated matter and energy exploded outward in all directions. At some point, clumps of matter came together to form stars and galaxies that are still moving away from one another today.

Materials

brown wrapping paper
marking pen
pencil
tape
metric ruler
watch or clock
soil, small stones, twigs, grass, and so forth

Procedure

1. On the floor, spread out a square sheet of brown wrapping paper measuring several meters on each side. **Note:** *You may need to tape together several sheets of paper in order to make a large enough square.*

2. Go outdoors and collect some soil, grass, small stones, twigs, and any other small natural items you find, such as acorns or seeds.

3. Use the items you have collected to make a lump of material a little larger than a golf ball. Using your hands, squeeze the soil and other items together tightly so that the lump is very dense. **Note:** *You may want to moisten the soil slightly.*

4. When you have squeezed the material as tightly as possible, hold it in your hand and stand directly above the square of paper. Hold your hand about a meter above the center of the square. With a quick, sharp movement, throw the ball of material onto the paper.

5. Locate what seems to be the center of the scattered material on the paper. Using a marking pen, mark the center with a large X. See Figure 1.

6. With a pencil, lightly mark the position of each piece of material on the paper.

7. Use a time interval of 1 minute. After 1 minute, move each piece of material outward in a straight line from the center a distance of 5 cm. Lightly mark the new positions with a pencil.

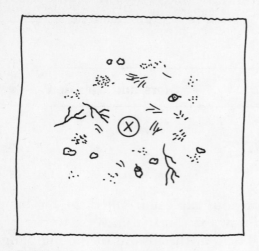

Figure 1

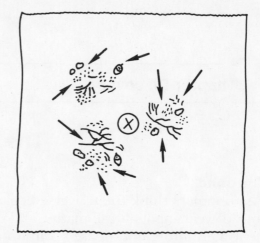

Figure 2

8. Repeat step 7. Then look at the arrangement of material on the paper. Find some large pieces of material with smaller pieces nearby. Move the smaller pieces toward the large pieces so that you form some large clumps. See Figure 2.

9. Continue moving the material outward from the center at a rate of 5 cm per minute as you did in step 7. Mark the new positions each time. Stop when you reach the edge of the paper.

Critical Thinking and Application

1. What state was the material in before it hit the paper?

_____

_____

2. What caused the material to hit the paper? What energy was involved?

_____

_____

3. What happened to the material when it hit the paper?

_____

_____

4. Throughout the remainder of the activity, how did the material change position? How was time a factor in these changes?

_____

_____

5. Imagine that the brown wrapping paper represents the universe and that each piece of material represents a planet, star, galaxy, or other object in the universe. Based on your observations in this activity, describe the formation and evolution of the universe.

_____

_____

_____

_____

_____

6. Assuming that the process you described in question 5 is still continuing, what is the state of the universe today? What do you think will happen to the universe in the future?

_____

_____

_____

_____

_____

_____

Activity

Naming Constellations

Ask your friends what sign they were born under and they can probably tell you immediately. These zodiac signs are actually the names ancient peoples gave to various constellations, or star groups. You will find a list of constellations below. However, in each case, either the constellation's name or its English equivalent has been left out. Fill in the constellation's name or its English equivalent in the appropriate space.

Constellation	**English Name**
1. Aquarius	_____
2. _____	Ram
3. Cancer	_____
4. Capricornus	_____
5. _____	Princess
6. Aquila	_____
7. _____	Swan
8. _____	Dragon
9. Gemini	_____
10. Hercules	_____
11. _____	Lion
12. Libra	_____
13. _____	Wolf
14. Hydra	_____
15. Orion	_____
16. _____	Winged horse
17. _____	Scorpion
18. Taurus	_____

19. Cassiopeia   _____

20. _____   Fish

21. Sagittarius   _____

22. _____   Great bear

23. Ursa Minor   _____

Activity

Early Astronomers

The people listed below made important contributions to the early history of astronomy. Using books and reference materials in the library, look up the following names and write a brief report about each scientist. Include the answers to the following questions: When and where did each scientist live? What was the major contribution of each scientist to astronomy?

In the space provided, outline the main ideas of your research and the answers to the questions.

Hypatia _____

_____

_____

Nicolaus Copernicus _____

_____

_____

_____

Tycho Brahe _____

_____

_____

_____

Johannes Kepler _____

_____

_____

_____

Galileo Galilei _____

_____

_____

_____

Activity

Drawing Constellations

The drawings below show the stars of some of the major constellations. Study the star patterns for each constellation and see if you can draw what ancient astronomers imagined when they named these constellations.

Capricornus

Sagittarius

Scorpius

Cancer

Leo

Cygnus

Ursa Minor

Draco

Ursa Major

Activity

The Hertzsprung-Russell Diagram

The Hertzsprung-Russell diagram is actually a graph that illustrates the relationship that exists between the average surface temperature of stars and their absolute magnitude, which is how bright they would appear to be if they were all the same distance away. Rather than speak of the brightness of stars, the term "luminosity" is often used. Luminosity is a measure of how much energy leaves a star in a certain period of time. Generally, for stars that are at equal distances from the Earth, the more luminous a star, the brighter it is.

The luminosity of stars is affected not only by temperature but also by size. The most luminous stars would be those that are large and hot. Those that are the least luminous would be small and cool. The color of a star is determined by its surface temperature, which is illustrated on the Hertzsprung-Russell diagram.

The Hertzsprung-Russell Diagram

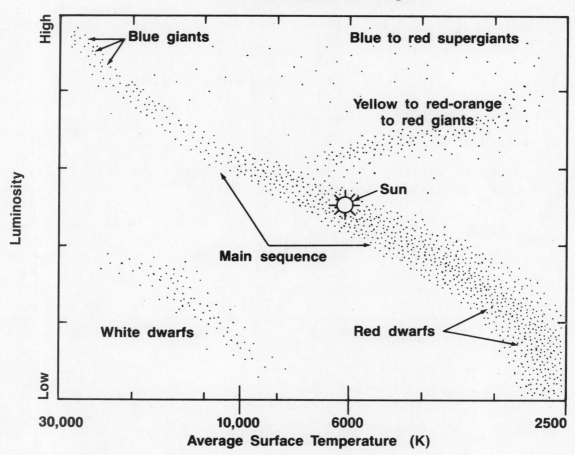

Using the Hertzsprung-Russell diagram provided in this activity, answer the following questions.

1. What is the approximate surface temperature of the sun? _____

2. Would the surface temperature of the stars classified as white dwarfs be generally

    higher or lower than that of stars classified as supergiants? _____

3. a. What is the color of the stars shown on the diagram that have the highest surface

        temperature? _____

    b. What is the color of the stars shown on the diagram that have the lowest surface

        temperature? _____

    c. List the colors of the stars from the color of the hottest star to the color of the
        coldest star:

                        Color of hottest star _____

                                              _____

                                              _____

                                              _____

                        Color of coldest star _____

4. Most of the stars shown on the diagram are classified as which type of star?

    _____

5. Our sun is classified as which type of star? _____

6. How is it possible for white dwarfs to have a lower luminosity than the sun even
    though the sun is much cooler than the white dwarfs?

    _____

    _____

    _____

    _____

Activity

Observing Circumpolar Constellations

Circumpolar constellations are those groups of star patterns that are always in view in the northern sky. These constellations appear to revolve about the North Star, Polaris. Polaris can easily be located in the evening sky by using the "pointer" stars of the Big Dipper constellation. The circumpolar constellation map illustrates some of the more visible circumpolar constellations.

Notice the position of the Big Dipper and the relationship between it and the North Star. Notice also that the names of the four seasons and the months of the year are printed around the edge of the chart. This will allow you to locate circumpolar constellations during the entire year.

Circumpolar Constellation Map

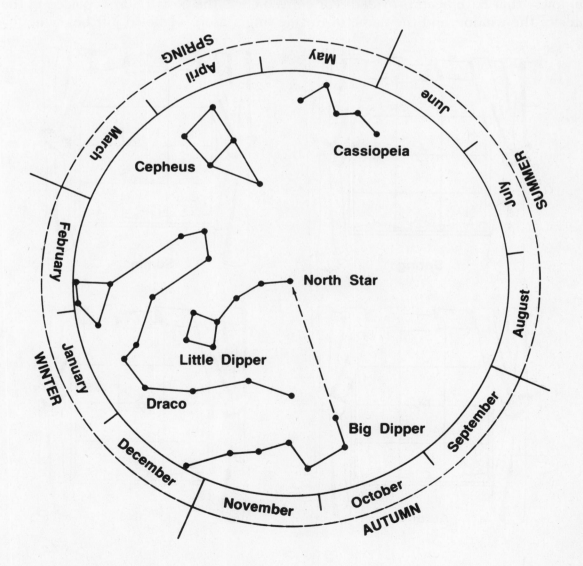

In order to use the map, turn it so that the month during which you are viewing is at the bottom. Each constellation is now positioned as you would see it at about 8 PM if you were facing north. Practice using the chart by answering the following questions:

1. During which season is the Big Dipper closest to the horizon? _____

2. Which constellation is highest in the sky during November? _____

3. Which constellation is highest in the sky in the spring? _____

4. During which month will the pointer stars of the Big Dipper point directly upward, away from the horizon? _____

5. In which constellation is the North Star located? _____

Refer again to the constellation map, turning it as necessary in order to make your observations. This time, make a sketch of the Big and Little Dipper constellations showing them positioned as they would be seen when viewed through a window facing north. Assume that the observations are made at four different times of the year, once during the middle of each season. Place your drawings within the sketches of the "windows" that have been provided. For convenience, the North Star is placed in the center of the window and the name of the viewing season is labeled just below it.

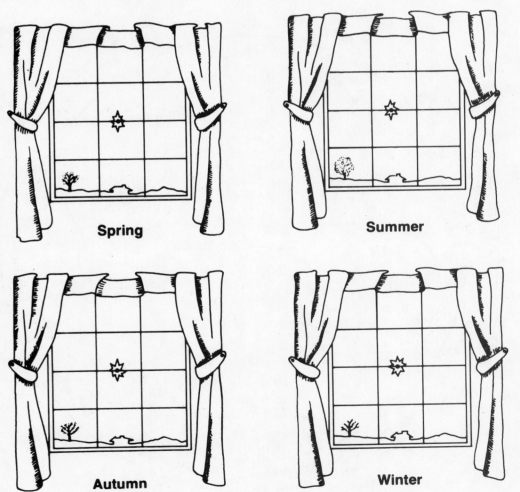

Spring

Summer

Autumn

Winter

Spectacular Night Sky

Interest in the night sky led primitive people to study the patterns of stars they saw and to give these patterns names. The patterns, or constellations, were named in honor of various mythological characters. In all, some 88 constellations have been identified. Some are easy to locate in the night sky while others are not. Can you think of some explanations for this?

The diagram below is a star chart of the spring sky in a particular location. The outer edge of the circle represents the horizon as the observer faces north, south, east, or west. To use the star chart, you would place the paper horizontally above your head and align the correct edge of the circle with the direction in which you are facing.

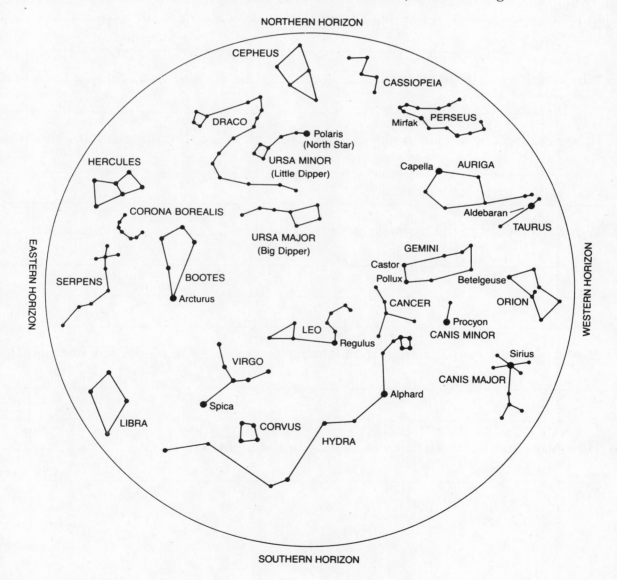

1. In which direction should you face to see the constellation Ursa Minor? _____

_____

2. What well-known star is the tip of the handle of Ursa Minor? _____

_____

3. Which constellation is directly overhead in spring? _____

_____

4. What is another name for the Big Dipper? _____

_____

5. How can you use the Big Dipper to find the Little Dipper? _____

_____

_____

6. In which constellation is the star Sirius located? _____

_____

7. Why is Sirius easy to identify? _____

_____

8. In which direction would an observer have to look to see the constellation Taurus?

_____

_____

9. Why do the stars in the night sky appear to twinkle? _____

_____

_____

_____

10. How many stars can be seen in the night sky by any one observer at any one time?

_____

_____

11. How many constellations can you identify in the night sky? _____

_____

Activity

Star Gazing

   Plan an evening of star gazing with your family or some friends. Study the information about stars and constellation patterns presented in this chapter to get some idea of what you will be trying to identify in the sky. Use the star charts in Appendix E, pages 157–160, or obtain a few detailed star charts from the library. The magazine *Sky and Telescope* contains star charts. Even an old star chart for the same month or season of the year will help. Only the planets and moon will have changed locations.

   Choose an area where you will be away from bright lights, and choose a clear night when the moon will not be very bright. The darker the sky, the easier it will be to see the stars.

   Draw sketches of the constellations that you see. Then name the constellations and label any stars or planets that you can identify.

Laboratory Investigation

Identifying Substances Using a Flame Test

Problem
How can substances be identified by using a flame test?

Materials *(per group)*
safety goggles
Bunsen burner
heat-resistant gloves
stainless steel teaspoon
1 unmarked bottle each of sodium chloride, potassium chloride, and lithium chloride

Procedure 🔥 ✋ 📷 👁

1. Put on the safety goggles. Carefully light the Bunsen burner. **CAUTION:** *If you are not sure how to light a Bunsen burner safely, have your teacher show you the correct procedure.*

2. Put on the heat-resistant gloves.

3. Place the tip of the clean teaspoon in water. Then dip the tip of the spoon into one of the unmarked powders. Make sure that some of the powder sticks to the wet tip.

4. Hold the tip of the spoon in the flame of the Bunsen burner until most of the powder has burned. Observe and record the color of the flame in the Data Table.

5. Repeat steps 3 and 4 using the powder in the second and third unmarked bottles. Observe and record the color of the flame for each powder.

Observations

DATA TABLE

Flame Test	Color of Flame	Name of Substance
Powder 1		
Powder 2		
Powder 3		

Analysis and Conclusions

1. Sodium chloride burns with a yellow flame. Potassium chloride burns with a purple flame. And lithium chloride burns with a red flame. Using this information, determine the identity of each of the unmarked powders. Record the names of the substances in the Data Table.

2. Why is it important to make sure the spoon is thoroughly cleaned before each flame test? Try the investigation without cleaning the spoon to test your answer.

_____

_____

_____

_____

_____

3. Relate this investigation to the way astronomers study a star's composition.

_____

_____

_____

_____

4. **On Your Own** Predict the color of the flame produced when various combinations of the three powders are used. With your teacher's permission, perform an investigation to test your prediction.

_____

_____

_____

_____

Answer Key

Chapter Discovery: The Big Bang

1. It was packed together into a small, dense ball. **2.** The material was thrown onto the paper. Energy was needed to throw the material onto the paper. **3.** It scattered outward in all directions. **4.** The material moved outward from the center at a rate of 5 cm per minute. Some smaller pieces of material clumped together with larger pieces. These clumps continued to move outward at a steady rate. **5.** The universe began as a small, dense clump of matter. Energy caused the clump to explode and break apart. After breaking apart, it began expanding outward at a steady rate. Smaller pieces of matter clumped together with larger pieces and the outward expansion continued. **6.** The universe today is still expanding. Accept all logical speculations for the future of the universe. Most scientists think that the big bang theory leads to two possible outcomes. In an "open" universe, the expansion would continue indefinitely. In a "closed" universe, the expansion would stop and gravity would pull matter back together again. Then another big bang would occur and a new universe would begin.

Activity: Naming Constellations

Note: *Be sure students understand that the astrological signs of the zodiac that people are "born under" have no basis in science.*
1. Water carrier **2.** Aries **3.** Crab
4. Goat **5.** Andromeda **6.** Eagle
7. Cygnus **8.** Draco **9.** Twins
10. Hercules **11.** Leo **12.** Scales
13. Lupus **14.** Water serpent **15.** Hunter
16. Pegasus **17.** Scorpius **18.** Bull
19. Queen **20.** Pisces **21.** Archer
22. Ursa Major **23.** Little bear

Activity: Early Astronomers

Hypatia (d. AD 415): daughter of Theon of Alexandria. A writer of mathematics; occupied the chair of Platonic philosophy in Alexandria; lectured on Plato and Aristotle. She wrote several mathematical and astronomical commentaries, which are now lost. **Nicolaus Copernicus** (1473–1543): Polish astronomer who developed the theory that the Earth is a moving planet; considered the founder of modern astronomy. Copernicus' theory on the movement of the Earth changed a belief, which was begun by Ptolemy and had existed for 1400 years, that the Earth was the center of the universe and had no motion. **Tycho Brahe** (1546–1601): Danish astronomer who successfully predicted a solar eclipse. His systematic observations of the planets night after night led to the discovery of a "new" star, or nova, in 1572 and proved that changes do occur in the solar system. He also showed that comets do not originate in the Earth's atmosphere but are bodies that move through outer space. **Johannes Kepler** (1571–1630): German astronomer and mathematician; discovered three laws of planetary motion, which formed an indispensable part of Isaac Newton's gravitational theory. Kepler's most important contribution to astronomy was the discovery that planets travel in elliptical orbits. **Galileo Galilei** (1563–1642): Italian astronomer and physicist; founder of modern experimental science. He developed and built larger and more powerful telescopes than had ever been used before. Using a telescope, he discovered that the moon is not a smooth sphere shining by its own light. He also observed that the Milky Way is a mass of stars. He discovered the four bright moons of Jupiter and observed the rings of Saturn.

Activity: Drawing Constellations

In this activity students are called upon to use their imagination and observational skills to identify common constellations and to draw the figures suggested by the names of the constellations. Accept all reasonable constellation drawings.

Activity: The Hertzsprung-Russell Diagram

1. about 6000 K 2. higher 3. a. blue
b. red c. blue, white, yellow, red-orange, red
4. main sequence 5. main sequence
6. White dwarfs are much smaller; luminosity depends on both size and temperature.

Activity: Observing Circumpolar Constellations

1. autumn 2. Cassiopeia 3. Big
Dipper 4. October 5. Little Dipper

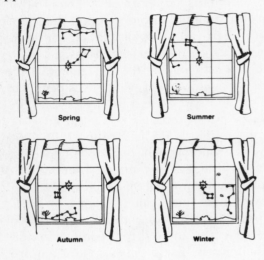

Activity: Spectacular Night Sky

1. north 2. Polaris (North Star) 3. Leo
4. Ursa Major 5. Use the pointer stars in the Big Dipper. They point to Polaris, the North Star, which is the tip of the handle of the Little Dipper. 6. Canis Major 7. It is the brightest star in the sky. 8. northwest
9. Stars seem to twinkle because starlight is shifted slightly by the constant movement of the Earth's atmosphere and by changes in air temperature and moisture. 10. 2000 with the unaided eye 11. Answers will vary.

Activity: Star Gazing

You can provide students with photographs of the constellations they will be able to see during the time they are studying this chapter. Explain the photographs and tell them the names of the constellations and individual stars. Point out any planets that are visible during this period.

Laboratory Investigation: Identifying Substances Using a Flame Test

Observations Students should observe that the color of the flames in the three tests are yellow, purple, and red. The identity of the substance in each test depends on the order in which the powders were used.

Analysis and Conclusions 1. Students should now be able to identify the three substances by color in the flame test. Sodium chloride burns yellow. Potassium chloride burns purple. Lithium chloride burns red. 2. It is important to clean the spoon after each test to avoid any contamination from powder remaining from a prior test. If students try performing the test without cleaning the spoon, they will find a mixture of colors in the flame when doing a flame test.
3. Students should now be able to relate their simple flame tests, which identify unknown substances, to the way astronomers identify the composition of a star with a spectroscope. You can point out at this time that if the students performed their flame tests again and observed the flames through a spectroscope, they would see characteristic spectral lines for the elements sodium, potassium, and lithium. 4. Predictions will vary, depending on the mixtures of various powders.

Contents

Chapter Discovery

Chapter Activities

Laboratory Investigation Worksheet

   (**Note:** *This investigation is found on page M98 of the student textbook.*)

Answer Key

*Appropriate for cooperative learning

Chapter Discovery

The Solar System

Making a Scale Model of the Solar System

Background

   The solar system formed from a swirling cloud of dust and gas about 5 billion years ago. Earth and the other eight planets that are part of the solar system revolve around the sun in elliptical orbits. In this activity you will make a scale model of the solar system showing the relative size of each planet and its relative distance from the sun.

Materials

open area at least 12 m × 12 m
metric ruler
meterstick
scissors
marking pen
tape
construction paper (yellow and other assorted colors)

Procedure

1. Cut a circle 1.4 m in diameter from a piece of yellow construction paper. **Note:** *You may have to tape together several pieces of construction paper to make a large enough circle.* This circle will represent the sun.

2. Choose a color other than yellow for each of the nine planets. **Note:** *You may use the same color more than once.* Cut a circle to represent each planet according to the dimensions listed below. Write the name of the planet on each circle.

Mercury	.4.9 mm
Venus	.12.0 mm
Earth	.12.8 mm
Mars	.6.8 mm
Jupiter	.142.8 mm
Saturn	.120.0 mm
Uranus	.50.8 mm
Neptune	.48.6 mm
Pluto	.3.0 mm

3. Choose an indoor or outdoor area at least 12 m × 12 m square. Possible areas might include a parking lot, a playground, a backyard, a park, a school gym, an auditorium, or a cafeteria.

4. Place the yellow circle representing the sun at the center of your area. Use a piece of tape to fasten the circle to the floor or whatever surface you are using.

5. Determine how far each planet should be placed from the sun by using the scale 1 mm = 1 million kilometers. Complete the chart on page 34, rounding the scale distance off to the nearest millimeter.

---

6. Place each planet at the correct distance from the sun according to the chart. Secure each planet with a piece of tape.

Planet	Distance from Sun (millions of km)	Scale Distance (mm)
Mercury	57.9	
Venus	108.2	
Earth	149.6	
Mars	227.9	
Jupiter	778.3	
Saturn	1427.0	
Uranus	2870.0	
Neptune	4497.0	
Pluto	5900.0	

Critical Thinking and Application

1. Which planet is closest to the sun? Which is farthest away?

_____

2. Look at the distances between the planets. Are the distances about the same? Or are some planets farther apart than others?

_____

_____

3. Although the relative sizes of the planets are accurate, they were not calculated using the same scale that was used to calculate the relative distances of the planets from the sun. What do you think would happen to your model if you used the same scale to measure distance from the sun as you used to determine the size of each planet? (*Hint*: The actual diameter of Mercury is 4878 km.)

_____

_____

_____

4. Based on your answer to question 3, can you explain why it is difficult to make a scale model of the solar system?

_____

_____

_____

Activity

How Big Is the Solar System?

The solar system is a very large structure. It is so large that it is difficult, if not impossible, to imagine. In this activity you will construct a scale model of the solar system and compare it to another large structure that you are more familiar with. To do so, you will need a pencil, a drawing compass, and a metric ruler.

Now follow the steps below to complete your scale model of the solar system.

1. The approximate distance from each planet to the sun is listed in the table at the right. Using the formula provided, convert each distance into the scale model distance. Place the scale model distances in the appropriate spaces in the table.

$$\text{Scale Model Distance (mm)} = \frac{\text{Actual Distance (in kilometers)}}{50{,}000{,}000 \text{ km}}$$

EXAMPLE: (for Mercury)

$$\text{Scale Model Distance (mm)} = \frac{57{,}900{,}000 \text{ km}}{50{,}000{,}000 \text{ km}}$$

$$\text{Scale Model Distance} = 1.158 \text{ mm}$$

Name of Planet	Distance From Sun	
	Actual Distance	Scale Model Distance
Mercury	57,900,000 km	1.16 mm
Venus	108,000,000 km	mm
Earth	149,000,000 km	mm
Mars	228,000,000 km	mm
Jupiter	778,000,000 km	mm
Saturn	1,430,000,000 km	mm
Uranus	2,870,000,000 km	mm
Neptune	4,500,000,000 km	mm
Pluto	5,900,000,000 km	mm

2. You can see from the example that while Mercury is actually about 57,900,000 km away from the sun in the solar system, it will only be 1.16 mm from the sun in the scale model solar system you are about to draw.

3. As accurately as possible, place a small dot that identifies the location of your school on the map of the United States on page 36. This dot will represent the sun in your scale model solar system. Label it as the sun.

4. Using a drawing compass and a metric ruler, draw the orbit that each planet would follow around the "sun" in your scale model. Use the scale model distances from the table as the radius distances for the appropriate orbit.

5. Label each orbit with the name of the planet that travels in the orbit. Your scale model of the solar system is now complete.

Scale

1 mm on map = 22.5 km of Earth distance

1 mm on map = 50,000,000 km of solar system distance

Activity

The Sun and Its Planets

The drawing below shows the nine planets that revolve around the sun. Identify each planet and write its name next to the corresponding letter in the chart. List the main features of each planet in the chart.

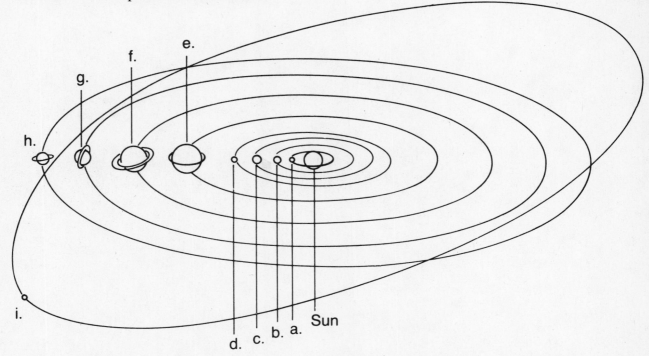

Planet	Main Features
a.	
b.	
c.	
d.	
e.	
f.	
g.	
h.	
i.	

Activity

Star Trails From a Rotating Earth

Imagine yourself lying on a blanket and looking up at the stars on a clear, dark night. You would be very surprised to see them all moving. Yet, if you stayed on that blanket for the whole night, that is exactly what you would see.

The stars appear to move because the Earth is rotating on its axis. Since the Earth turns 360° in 24 hours, any point on its surface moves at a rate of 15° (360° ÷ 24) each hour. The stars will seem to move at this same rate.

Usually this movement of the stars is unnoticed, unless the observer views the sky for hours at a time. It is possible, however, to make simple indirect observations of apparent star motion through the use of a camera. This can be accomplished by taking a time exposure. The camera is set in a fixed position with the shutter left open for a longer time than usual. Light from stars that enters the camera's lens will produce curved lines on the film. These curved lines trace the apparent paths of those stars. Star path pictures produced in this fashion are called star trails.

If the camera is directed toward Polaris, the North Star, star trails that result are of particular interest. Each star trail that is produced forms part of a circle, or arc, that has the North Star at its center. The longer the camera shutter is open, the longer the arcs are that are formed. If an exposure lasted for 24 hours, then the arcs would become full circles centered about Polaris. If the camera shutter was left open for 12 hours, each arc would be exactly half a circle, or 180°. Therefore, the length of the arc, in degrees, is a measure of how long the film was left exposed. Now let's take a look at some star trails. To do so, you will need a protractor.

Procedure

1. Examine the sketches of both sets of star trails in Figures 1 and 2 on the following page. Each diagram represents star trails that were made by cameras which had their shutters left open for different lengths of time. In each case the cameras were directed toward the North Star.

2. Refer to Figure 1. Use the straight edge of your protractor to draw a line from the center (Polaris) of the set of star trails to the end of any arc. Construct a second line from the center to the other end of the same arc.

3. Using a protractor, determine the size of the angle formed by the lines drawn to the two ends of the arc. This angle represents the distance, in degrees, that the Earth turned on its axis during the time that the film was exposed. Record your answer in the proper place in the Data Table.

4. Repeat the process for an arc formed by any other star found in Figure 1.

5. Determine the average for these two values and enter it in the proper place in the Data Table.

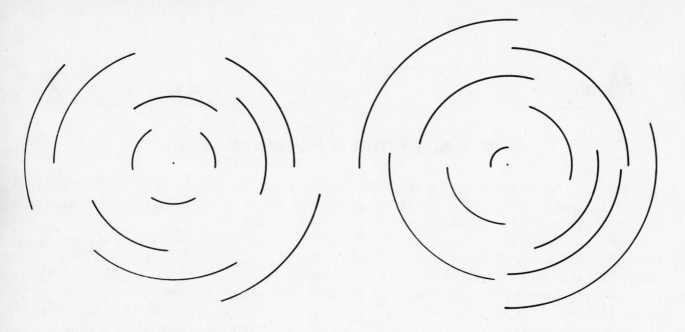

Figure 1

Figure 2

6. Calculate the duration of the exposure, in hours, that was used to record the star trails found in Figure 1.

7. Now repeat steps 2 through 6 using the star trails in Figure 2.

DATA TABLE		Length of Star Trail in Degrees		Duration of Exposure in Hours
Figure 1	First star trail		Average	
	Second star trail			
Figure 2	First star trail		Average	
	Second star trail			

Critical Thinking and Application

1. Why do you think that Polaris is the only star in the northern sky that does not seem to produce a star trail?

_____

2. If stars do not really move, why do they seem to move?

_____

_____

3. A bright star is observed in the evening sky. At the end of 3 hours, how many

degrees will this star appear to have moved? _____

Activity

Inertia Versus Gravity

1. Tape a length of string to a Ping-Pong ball. The string represents the gravitational pull of the sun, which keeps objects in orbit.

2. Swing the string with the ball attached over your head. **CAUTION:** *Make sure you do not swing the ball near anyone.*

3. Swing the string again. When you are sure no classmate is nearby, let go of the string.

Describe the actions of the ball using the word inertia. _____

_____

Relate this activity to the two factors that cause planets to travel in elliptical orbits.

_____

_____

_____

_____

_____

   In the space provided, draw a diagram to illustrate the movement of the ball in step 2. Use arrows to indicate the two factors, or forces, acting on the ball. Draw another diagram illustrating the movement of the ball in step 3. Here again use arrows to indicate the forces affecting the ball's motion. Should one arrow be larger than the other?

Activity

"Backward" Motion of Planets

Planets tend to move across the sky in an easterly direction. Occasionally, something strange occurs. A planet appears to slow down and begin moving backward toward the west. In this activity you are going to find out why this happens.

The diagram below represents a part of our solar system. Earth and Mars are shown at several positions in their orbits around the sun. Each position is labeled with the name of the month when the planet will be located there.

Procedure

1. In the diagram below, draw a line from each Earth position through the Mars position for the same month. Extend the line approximately 1 cm past the dashed line. Place a dot at the end of the line and label the dots in order, with the dot on the January line being number 1, the dot on the February line being number 2, and so on. **Note:** *Draw the lines that pass through the May and June positions slightly longer and place the dots slightly farther away than you did for the other lines.* Notice that the line for January is already drawn and the dot is labeled.

2. Using a pencil, start with the dot labeled "1" and carefully connect the dots in order. This line represents the path the planet Mars would follow in its orbit around the sun as seen from Earth.

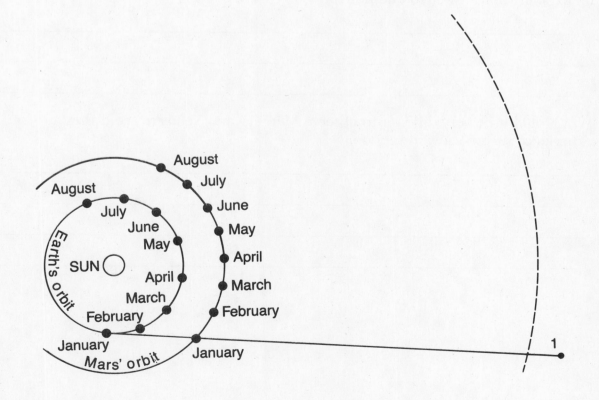

The dots that you put at the ends of the lines represent the positions where an observer on Earth would see Mars for the month indicated on the diagram. The line you drew connecting the dots represents the path Mars appears to follow.

Critical Thinking and Application

1. a. What movement does Mars actually experience from January through August?

_____

   b. To an observer on Earth, what movement does Mars appear to experience during that time period?

_____

2. During which of the following months does Mars appear to be moving backward in

   its orbit? _____

   a. January   b. March   c. May   d. July

3. Carefully observe what is happening to Earth and Mars in their orbits when Mars seems to loop "backward." What causes Mars to seem to move backward in its orbit?

_____

_____

4. a. Do you think that to an observer on Earth all the planets visible in the night sky

   would appear at some point to go backward? _____

   b. Explain your answer to question 4a.

_____

_____

_____

5. Why would it be very difficult to observe Mercury and Venus to see if they experience such backward motion?

_____

_____

_____

Laboratory Investigation

Constructing a Balloon Rocket

Problem
How can a balloon rocket be used to illustrate Newton's third law of motion?

Materials *(per group)*
drinking straw
scissors
9-m length of string
balloon
masking tape
meterstick

Procedure ▆▆

1. Cut the drinking straw in half. Pull the string through one of the halves.
2. Blow up the balloon and hold the end so that the air does not escape.
3. Have someone tape the drinking straw with the string pulled through it to the side of the balloon as shown in the diagram on page 46. Do not let go of the balloon.
4. Have two students pull the string tight between them.
5. Move the balloon to one end of the string. Release the balloon and observe its flight toward the other end of the string.
6. Record the flight number and distance the balloon traveled in the Data Table.
7. Repeat the flight of the balloon four more times. Record each flight number and length in the Data Table.

Observations

DATA TABLE

Flight	Distance
1	
2	
3	
4	
5	

1. What was the longest flight of your balloon rocket? The shortest flight? _____

2. What was the average distance reached by your balloon? _____

Analysis and Conclusions

1. Using Newton's third law of motion, explain what caused the movement of the

   balloon. _____

   _____

   _____

2. Compare your balloon rocket to the way a real rocket works. _____

   _____

   _____

3. Suppose your classmates obtained different results for the distances their balloons

   traveled. What variables may have caused the differences? _____

   _____

   _____

4. **On Your Own** As you have read, rockets require a certain thrust to escape Earth's
   gravitational pull. How might you increase the thrust of your balloon rocket? Try it

   and see if you are correct. _____

   _____

   _____

Masking tape   Straw   String

Balloon

Answer Key

Chapter Discovery: Making a Scale Model of the Solar System

Chart: Mercury = 58 mm; Venus = 108 mm; Earth = 150 mm; Mars = 228 mm; Jupiter = 778 mm; Saturn = 1427 mm; Uranus = 2870 mm; Neptune = 4497 mm; Pluto = 5900 mm **1.** Mercury; Pluto **2.** The four inner planets—Mercury, Venus, Earth, Mars—are about the same distance apart, but then there is a very large gap between Mars and Jupiter. The distance between Saturn and Uranus is about twice the distance between Jupiter and Saturn. The distance between Uranus and Neptune, and between Neptune and Pluto, is about the same as the distance between Saturn and Uranus. **3.** The model of the solar system would stretch across an entire town, because at a scale of 1 mm = 1000 km, Pluto would be 5.9 million millimeters, or 5.9 km, from the sun. **4.** If the planets are large enough to be seen, the distances become enormous. If the distances of the planets from the sun are reasonable, the planets become ridiculously small.

Activity: How Big Is the Solar System?

1. Venus: 2.16 mm; Earth: 2.98 mm; Mars: 4.56 mm; Jupiter: 15.56 mm; Saturn: 28.60 mm; Uranus: 57.40 mm; Neptune: 90.00 mm; Pluto: 118.00 mm **3.** Students may need a state map or an atlas to help them locate their school. **4.** Be certain students place the point of the compass in the center of the "sun" they plotted on the map. **5.** If students are concerned because they have been instructed to draw circles to represent elliptical orbits, remind them that the orbits are only slightly elliptical and would appear circular at the scale they draw them. Because of the location of some schools, some of the orbits will, in fact, be only arcs.

Activity: The Sun and Its Planets

a. Mercury: closest to the sun; rocky, cratered surface; extremely thin hydrogen, helium, and sodium atmosphere **b.** Venus: retrograde rotation; thick cloud cover; greenhouse effect; carbon dioxide atmosphere **c.** Earth: liquid water; supports life; nitrogen and oxygen atmosphere; one moon **d.** Mars: rust-colored surface; pink sky; polar ice caps; carbon dioxide, nitrogen, argon, oxygen, and water vapor atmosphere; two moons **e.** Jupiter: largest planet; Great Red Spot; thin ring; huge magnetosphere; hydrogen, helium, methane, and ammonia atmosphere; 16 moons **f.** Saturn: many rings and ringlets; one of its moons has a substantial atmosphere (Titan); hydrogen, helium, methane, and ammonia atmosphere; probably has 23 moons **g.** Uranus: rotates on its side; nine narrow rings; retrograde rotation; hydrogen, helium, and methane atmosphere; five moons **h.** Neptune: unusual satellite rotation; probably has two rings; hydrogen, helium, and methane atmosphere; two moons **i.** Pluto: smallest planet; methane atmosphere; possibly a double planet; one moon (Charon)

Activity: Star Trails From a Rotating Earth

The answers in the Data Table will vary depending on the arcs chosen. The following data refer to the simple arcs indicated in Figures 1 and 2. **Figure 1** first star trail: 59°; second star trail: 61°; average: 60°; duration: 4 hours **Figure 2** first star trail: 89°; second star trail: 91°; average: 90°; duration: 6 hours **1.** The north polar axis of Earth points toward Polaris so stars seem to revolve around Polaris as Earth turns on its axis. **2.** The rotation of the Earth causes the background of stars to appear to move. **3.** 45°

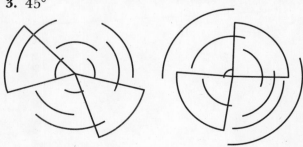

Figure 1   Figure 2

Activity: Inertia Versus Gravity

Like all moving objects, the ball (planet) has a tendency to move in a straight line unless acted upon by an outside force. This tendency is called inertia. In this case, the outside force—the string (sun's gravitational pull)—keeps the ball (planet) moving in a curved path (orbit). Once the string is released (the sun's gravitational pull is removed), the ball (planet) flies off in a straight line.

Activity: "Backward" Motion of Planets

1. a. It revolves counterclockwise in its orbit around the sun. b. It appears to loop backward in its orbit for a period of time (retrograde motion).   2. c   3. Mars appears to move backward as the Earth overtakes Mars and passes it in its orbit. Soon after the Earth passes Mars, the backward, or retrograde, motion stops.   4. a. Yes. b. All of the planets have different periods of revolution and move at different speeds in their orbits. Therefore, the planets will pass each other in their orbits. Retrograde motion is visible to an observer on Earth when Earth passes another planet in its orbit.   5. The orbits of Mercury and Venus place them between Earth and the sun. In order for observers on Earth to see retrograde motion of Mercury or Venus, they would have to look at or near the sun. **CAUTION:** *Remind students that they should never look directly at the sun; it can be extremely dangerous to the eyes.*

Laboratory Investigation: Constructing a Balloon Rocket

Observations   1. Answers will vary.
2. Answers will vary. Make sure students understand how to find an average distance by dividing the total distance by the number of trials.   **Analysis and Conclusions**
1. Students will observe that the movement of the balloon along the string is caused by air escaping through the open end of the balloon. The action of the air rushing out of the end of the balloon causes an opposite reaction on the balloon, and it moves forward. Thus, the balloon rocket obeys Newton's third law of motion.   **2.** In a rocket engine hot gases are produced by the rapid burning of a fuel in the engine's combustion chamber. As hot gases are released downward, the pressure of the gases on the front of the combustion chamber causes the rocket to move upward.   **3.** Most of the balloons will not move at the same speed. Some of the variables that may affect the flight of the balloons are the sizes and shapes of the balloons, how much air is in the balloons, and how tautly the strings are held.   **4.** Answers will vary. Students might try blowing more air into the balloon, making their release quicker, or altering the flight path in some way.

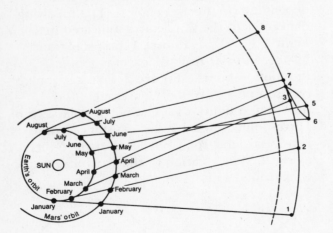

Contents

*Appropriate for cooperative learning

Phases of the Moon

Background
The moon takes 29.5 days to revolve around the Earth. During this time, the moon you see in the sky appears to change shape. These apparent changes, which are called phases, occur because the moon changes position relative to the Earth and sun. The relative positions of the moon, Earth, and sun determine how much of the moon is illuminated by sunlight. In this activity you will model the phases of the moon.

Materials
Styrofoam ball
knitting needle
lamp

Procedure
1. Carefully stick the point of the knitting needle into the Styrofoam ball so that the needle forms a "handle" for the ball. The Styrofoam ball will represent the moon.
2. Turn on the lamp. The lamp will represent the sun.
3. Pull down the shades and turn off any other lights in the room.
4. Imagine that you are an observer on Earth looking at the moon. Hold the knitting needle at arm's length so that the "moon" (Styrofoam ball) is between your eyes and the lamp. How much of the part of the ball facing you is illuminated by the lamp? How much of the part of the ball facing you is in darkness?

_____

_____

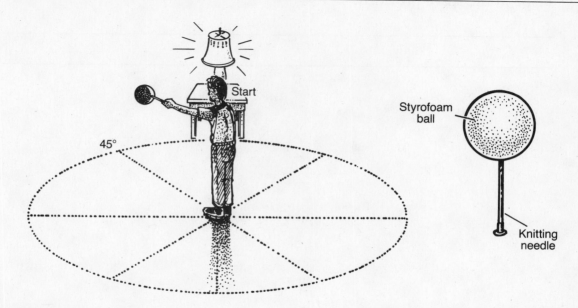

Figure 1

5. Turn your body 45° to the left. See Figure 1. Keep the ball directly in front of you at arm's length. How much of the ball is now illuminated? In the space provided, draw the shape of the lighted portion of the ball that you can see.

_____

_____

6. Make another 45° turn to the left as shown in Figure 1. Keep the ball in front of you at arm's length. How much of the lighted ball can you see now? Draw the lighted portion of the ball in the space provided.

_____

_____

7. Make another 45° turn to the left. How much of the ball is visible now? Draw its shape in the space provided.

_____

_____

8. Make another 45° turn to the left so that the lamp is directly behind you. Hold the ball in front of you at arm's length, but be sure your body does not block the light from falling on the ball. How much of the part of the ball facing you is visible now? Draw its shape in the space provided.

_____

_____

9. Make another 45° turn to the left. What happens to the lighted part of the ball? Draw the shape that you see in the space provided. Is this shape similar to any other shape you have drawn?

_____

_____

10. Make another 45° turn to the left. How much of the ball is lighted now? Draw the shape that you see.

_____

_____

11. Make another 45° turn to the left. Draw the shape of the lighted portion of the ball. Is this shape similar to any other shape you have drawn?

_____

_____

12. Make another 45° turn so that you are once again facing the lamp. What happens to the lighted portion of the ball?

_____

_____

Critical Thinking and Applications

1. How many phases of the moon are there?

_____

2. What causes these phases?

_____

_____

_____

3. Which phases of the moon are similar in shape?

_____

_____

4. When the moon is in total darkness, the phase is called a new moon. Beginning with the new moon, list in order the shapes of the moon that are visible as the moon revolves around the Earth.

_____

_____

_____

Activity

Phases of the Moon

Choose the phase of the moon from the list below and write it on the appropriate line in the drawing.

first quarter	waning crescent
full	waning gibbous
last quarter	waxing crescent
new	waxing gibbous

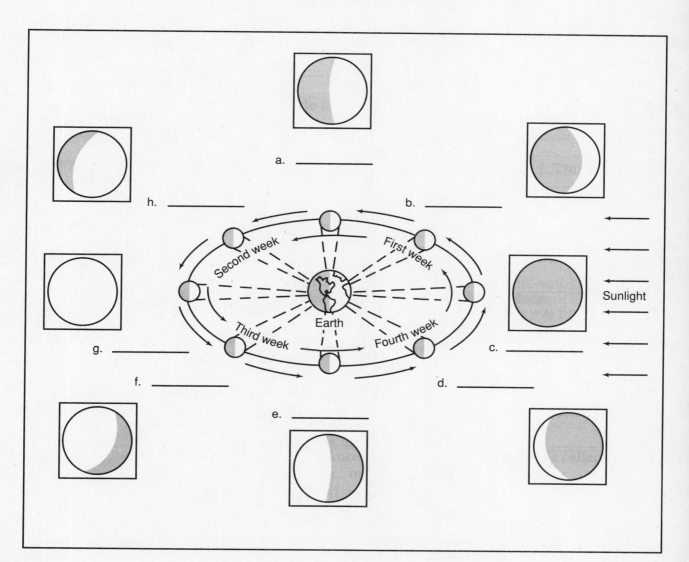

Lunar and Solar Eclipses

The two drawings below depict either a lunar or a solar eclipse. Identify which drawing refers to which type of eclipse. Then fill in the correct term beside each letter.

1. _____ eclipse

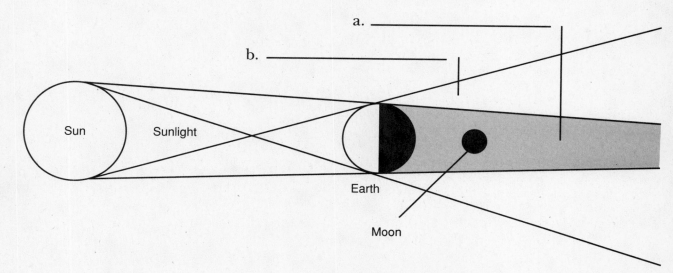

2. _____ eclipse

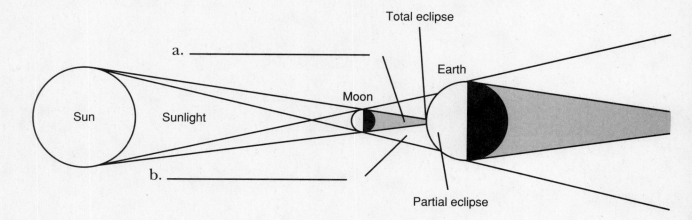

Activity

High and Low Tides

Because the moon is close to the Earth, there are interactions between the Earth and the moon. One visible interaction is the effect of the gravitational pull of the moon on the Earth. This pull results in the rise and fall of the ocean level as the moon moves in its orbit around the Earth. The rise and fall of the oceans are called tides.

Use Figure 1 to answer questions 1 and 2.

1. Which side of the Earth is facing the moon?

_____

2. Which sides of the Earth are having

low tide? _____

High tide? _____

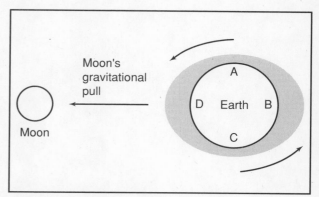

Figure 1

Use Figure 2 to answer questions 3 and 4.

3. Which sides of the Earth are having

low tide? _____

High tide? _____

4. How much time has passed between

Figures 1 and 2? _____

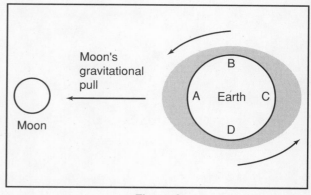

Figure 2

Use Figure 3 to answer questions 5 and 6.

5. Which sides of the Earth are having

high tide? _____

Low tide? _____

6. How much time has passed between

Figures 2 and 3? _____

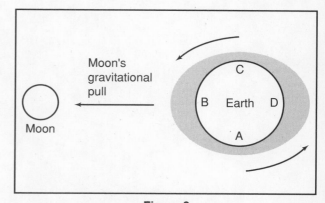

Figure 3

Activity

Spring and Neap Tides

Part A Spring Tides

When the moon is at its full and new phases, the Earth has higher high tides and lower low tides than at other times. These tides are called spring tides and they occur twice a month, when the sun and the moon line up with the Earth. The increased effect of the sun's gravity on the Earth causes the ocean bulges to become larger.

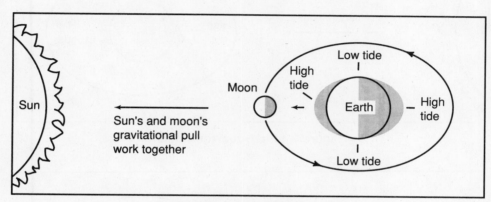

Figure 1   New moon

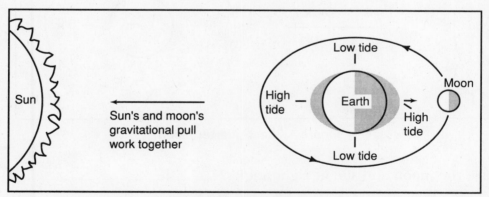

Figure 2   Full moon

1. When are the sun, moon, and Earth in a line? _____

_____

2. What happens to the pull of gravity on the Earth when the sun, Earth, and moon are in a line?

_____

3. What are the unusually high and low tides called? _____

4. How often do the unusually high and low tides occur? _____

5. At which moon phases do the spring tides take place? _____

_____

Part B Neap Tides

During the first- and last-quarter phases, the moon's gravitational pull on the oceans is partially canceled out by the sun's gravitational pull. This results in tides that are not very high and not very low. These tides are called neap tides and they occur twice a month.

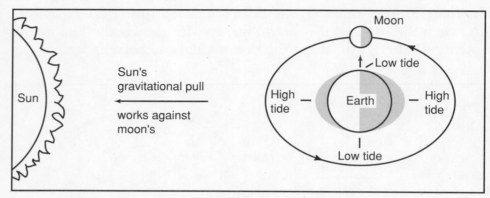

Figure 3   First-quarter moon

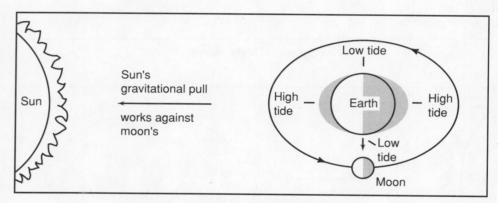

Figure 4   Last-quarter moon

1. When are the moon and sun at right angles? _____

_____

2. What happens to the pull of gravity when the moon and sun are at right angles?

_____

3. What kinds of tides occur when the moon and sun are at right angles? _____

_____

4. What are tides that are not very high and not very low called? _____

5. How often do these tides occur? _____

6. At which moon phases do these tides take place? _____

_____

Activity

Earth and Its Moon

CHAPTER
3

Tracking the Sun Across the Sky

Our sun is the nearest star to the Earth. But it is only one of the billions of stars that dot the heavens. This star is very important because it provides the energy we need to survive. The sun is a sphere of extremely hot gases.

The Earth revolves around the sun in an elliptical orbit. The Earth's distance from the sun changes slightly from month to month and season to season. The average distance between the Earth and the sun is about 150,000,000 km. Each day the sun appears to move from east to west across the sky. But it is the rotation of the Earth from west to east that makes the sun appear to move across the sky.

The sun rises higher in the sky in the summer than it does in the spring and fall because it progresses northward in the sky as summer approaches. In the winter, the sun rises to its lowest height in the sky.

Figure 1 shows the different heights to which the sun rises during the four seasons of the year. By following the shadow the sun casts on the Earth during the day, we can track the sun across the sky.

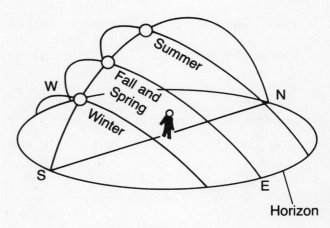

Figure 1

On a clear fall day, the sun was tracked across the sky by using a setup similar to the one shown in Figure 2. The sun shone on the pencil, producing a shadow on the cardboard. As the Earth beneath the cardboard rotated to the east, the shadow changed each hour.

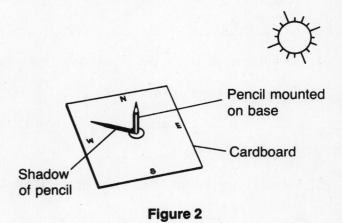

Figure 2

On the graph paper provided, plot the values given in the following Data Table. These values represent the positions of the sun over a period of 8 hours. Write the time next to each plotted point. Also plot the position of the pencil. Connect all of the points on the graph with a smooth line. Measure the length of the pencil shadow for each hour and record your answers in the Data Table.

DATA TABLE

Time	X-axis Value	Y-axis Value	Pencil Shadow (Length)
8:00 AM	29	2	
9:00 AM	21	15	
10:00 AM	17	23	
11:00 AM	16	29	
12:00 noon	14.5	35	
1:00 PM	13.5	41	
2:00 PM	13	46	
Pencil location	1	31	

1. How long is the pencil shadow at noon? _____ At what hour is the shadow longest? _____ Why is the shadow longest at this hour? _____

_____

_____

2. Based on the line you have drawn on the graph, describe the path of the sun across the sky.

_____

_____

3. In what direction is the pencil shadow pointing at 8:00 AM? _____

Where in the sky would the sun be located at that hour? _____

_____

4. At what hour is the pencil shadow the shortest? _____ Why is the shadow shortest at this hour? _____

_____

_____

5. Why are the summer months in a state such as Texas hotter than the winter months?

_____

_____

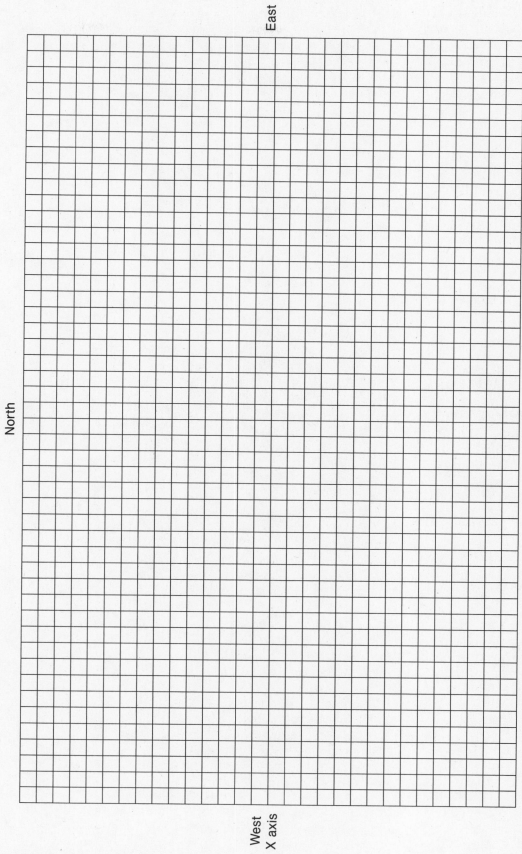

Path of the Sun Across the Sky

East

North

South
Y axis

West
X axis

Laboratory Investigation

Chapter 3 ■ Earth and Its Moon

Observing the Apparent Motion of the Sun

Problem
How can the sun's apparent motion in the sky be determined by observing changes in the length and direction of a shadow?

Materials *(per student)*
wooden stick and base
piece of cardboard, 25 cm × 25 cm
compass
wide-tip felt pen
metric ruler

Procedure ■■
1. Place the stick attached to a base in the middle of a piece of cardboard. Trace the outline of the base on the cardboard so that you will be able to put it in the same position each time you make an observation of the sun.

2. Place the stick and the cardboard on flat ground in a sunny spot.

3. Using the compass, locate north, south, east, and west. Write the appropriate directions near the edges of the cardboard.

4. With the felt pen, trace the shadow of the stick on the cardboard. Write the time of day along the line. Measure the length of the shadow. Determine in which direction the shadow is pointing. Determine the position of the sun in the sky. **CAUTION:** *Do not look directly at the sun!* Record your observations in the Data Table on page 70.

5. Repeat step 4 five more times throughout the day. Be sure to include morning, noon, and afternoon observations.

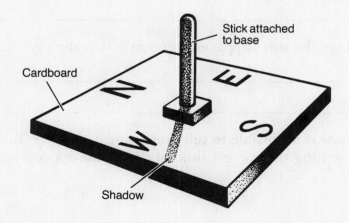

Stick attached to base

Cardboard

Shadow

Observations

DATA TABLE

Time of Day	Shadow Length	Direction of Shadow	Location of Sun

1. In which direction does the sun appear to move across the sky? _____

_____

_____

2. In which direction does the shadow move? _____

_____

_____

3. At what time of day is the shadow the longest? The shortest? _____

_____

_____

Analysis and Conclusions

1. Why does the length of the shadow change during the day? _____

_____

_____

2. What actually causes the sun's apparent motion across the sky? _____

_____

_____

3. **On Your Own** How is it possible to tell time using a sundial? Turn your shadow stick into a sundial by writing the correct time of day in the appropriate places on the cardboard.

Answer Key

Chapter Discovery: Phases of the Moon

Step 4. The entire half of the ball facing the student is in darkness. **Step 5.** One eighth of the ball (the right side) is illuminated. Student drawings should show a crescent shape facing to the left. **Step 6.** One quarter of the ball, or half a circle (the right side), is visible now. **Step 7.** Students should see three quarters of a circle (the right side). **Step 8.** The entire half of the ball facing the student should now be visible. Student drawings should show a full circle. **Step 9.** Three quarters of a circle (the left side) should be visible. The shape is the same as in Step 7, except that the illuminated part of the circle is on the left instead of the right. **Step 10.** One quarter of the ball, or half a circle (the left side) is lighted. **Step 11.** The shape is a crescent, as in Step 5, but facing in the opposite direction. **Step 12.** The lighted portion of the ball is now in shadow. Once again, the entire half of the ball facing the student is in darkness. **Critical Thinking and Application** **1.** Eight **2.** The phases of the moon are caused by the position of the moon relative to the sun and to the Earth, which determines which part of the moon reflects sunlight. **3.** The two crescent phases, the two half-circle or quarter phases, and the two three-quarter circle or gibbous phases are similar in shape. **4.** New moon (no shape visible), crescent (right side), half circle (right side), three-quarter circle (right side), full circle, three-quarter circle (left side), half circle (left side), crescent (left side), new moon.

Activity: Phases of the Moon

a. first quarter **b.** waxing crescent **c.** new **d.** waning crescent **e.** last quarter **f.** waning gibbous **g.** full **h.** waxing gibbous

Activity: Lunar and Solar Eclipses

1. Lunar **a.** umbra **b.** penumbra **2.** Solar **a.** umbra **b.** penumbra

Activity: High and Low Tides

1. D **2.** A and C, B and D **3.** B and D, A and C **4.** 6 hours **5.** B and D, A and C **6.** 6 hours

Activity: Spring and Neap Tides

Part A. 1. new- and full-moon phases **2.** The pull of gravity becomes stronger. **3.** spring tides **4.** twice a month **5.** new- and full-moon phases **Part B. 1.** first- and last-quarter phases **2.** The pull of gravity becomes weaker. **3.** not very high tides and not very low tides **4.** neap tides **5.** twice a month **6.** first- and last-quarter phases

Activity: Tracking the Sun Across the Sky

Table (length in cm): 15.0; 9.0; 7.6; 7.1; 8.2; 9.7 **Graph:** should correspond to information in the Data Table **1.** 7.1 cm; 8:00 AM. The sun is at a low point in the morning sky, casting a long shadow. **2.** The line shows that the sun makes a curved path across the sky. **3.** northwest; southeast **4.** Noon. The sun is almost directly overhead, casting a short shadow. **5.** The sun rises higher in the sky during the summer months, allowing more direct rays to strike the Earth's surface and causing more heat. In the winter months, when the sun rises lower in the sky, slanting rays strike the Earth, causing less heat.

Laboratory Investigation: Observing the Apparent Motion of the Sun

Observations 1. East to west. **2.** West to east. **3.** Longest: morning and late afternoon; shortest: noon, or 11 AM during daylight saving time. **Analysis and Conclusions** **1.** The shadow length varies due to shifts in the angles between the sun and the stick. **2.** Earth's rotation on its axis from west to east. **3.** A sundial is essentially similar to the students' setups. If the setups are in the correct spots in relation to the sun, the shadow will emulate the hours of the day.

Science Reading Skills

TO THE TEACHER

One of the primary goals of the *Prentice Hall Science* program is to help students acquire skills that will improve their level of achievement in science. Increasing awareness of the thinking processes associated with communicating ideas and reading content materials for maximum understanding are two skills students need in order to handle a more demanding science curriculum. Teaching reading skills to junior high school students at successive grade levels will help ensure the mastery of science objectives. A review of teaching patterns in secondary science courses shows a new emphasis on developing concept skills rather than on accumulating factual information. The material presented in this section of the Activity Book serves as a vehicle for the simultaneous teaching of science reading skills and science content.

The activities in this section are designed to help students develop specific science reading skills. The skills are organized into three general areas: comprehension skills, study skills, and vocabulary skills. The Science Gazette at the end of the textbook provides the content material for learning and practicing these reading skills. Each Science Gazette article has at least one corresponding science reading skill exercise.

Contents

Name _____ Class _____ Date _____

Ian K. Shelton Discovers an Exploding Star
Science Reading Skill: Defining Technical Terms

Perhaps you have had difficulty with some of the scientific terms that you have come across in reading science material. One skill that can help you find the meaning of scientific terms is using context clues. In this technique, you find a phrase or sentence that describes, gives an example of, or states the meaning of the word. From this phrase or sentence comes a definition of the word.

Part A

Listed below are several scientific terms used in this article. Use the skill of finding word meanings from context clues to write a definition of each term. Write your definition on the lines next to each word. The paragraph in which each word is used is indicated in the parentheses. If the words are totally new to you and you cannot determine the meaning from the context, refer to the glossary in the back of your science textbook or to a dictionary. Be sure to find the scientific meaning of the term as it is used in the article.

1. galaxy (paragraph 1) _____

    _____

2. astronomers (paragraph 4) _____

    _____

3. supernovas (paragraph 6) _____

    _____

4. matter (paragraph 6) _____

    _____

5. fuse (paragraph 7) _____

    _____

6. elements (paragraph 9) _____

    _____

7. hemoglobin (paragraph 9) _____

    _____

Part B

For each of the words you have defined, write a sentence in which you use the word with its meaning as it appears in the article.

1. _____

_____

2. _____

_____

3. _____

_____

4. _____

_____

5. _____

_____

6. _____

_____

7. _____

_____

Science Reading Skill: Sequence of Events

The following is a list of events that are described in this article. After reading all of the events, arrange them in the order in which they occurred. Write the letter of the event on the blank line next to the number that represents its sequence. In other words, put the letter of the event that occurred first on the blank next to the number one, and so on.

1. _____   a. Shelton went outside and saw the supernova without a telescope.

2. _____   b. Shelton sent telegrams to astronomers all over the world.

3. _____   c. The discovery was named Supernova 1987A.

4. _____   d. A giant star explodes in a galaxy 170,000 light years away.

5. _____   e. Shelton decided to develop one last photograph.

Science Gazette: Issues in Science

Exploring the Universe

Looking for Life Beyond Earth
Science Reading Skill: Previewing

A very important skill in studying science is knowing how to preview material. Previewing is actually preparing to receive the information you will be reading.

Previewing science material gives you an idea of the topics that will be discussed, the way in which the information is presented, and what you will be expected to learn. Developing this previewing skill will enable you to increase your understanding of scientific concepts.

Using this article, follow the steps below to learn the technique of previewing.

1. Read the title. A title may be a clue to what the article is about.

2. Look at all illustrations and read their captions. An illustration provides another clue to understanding the content of the article.

3. Read the first paragraph, the first sentence of all the following paragraphs, and then the entire last paragraph.

If you have followed these steps you should already have a very good idea of the main points of the article. Now answer the preview question by circling the correct choice.

Your preview of this article tells you that it is mostly about
   a. evidence of the existence of other planetary systems.
   b. radio waves given off by stars and planets.
   c. the possibility that intelligent life exists elsewhere in the universe.
   d. how "E.T." was made into a popular movie.

Science Reading Skill: Reading Comprehension

Reading comprehension is the result of a complex activity that uses many reading skills. It involves thinking, predicting, and evaluating. First, it is most important to know the purpose of your reading. Ask yourself, "What am I learning by reading this article?" This is an excellent way to help you determine the main points of the article, and to better understand the science material you read.

Now that you have read this article, see how well you can answer the following questions. Use complete sentences in writing your answers on the lines provided.

1. What is the main idea discussed in this article? _____

_____

_____

_____

2. What special feature is attributed to the planet Earth? _____

_____

3. Why do some biologists believe that the planet Earth is unique? _____

_____

_____

_____

4. Dr. Carl Sagan, a noted astronomer, said: "Absence of evidence is not evidence of absence." In connection with the question of the existence of intelligent life on other planets, explain Dr. Sagan's statement. _____

_____

_____

5. What suggestion did Philip Morrison make about how alien civilizations might communicate with Earth? _____

_____

_____

6. What are some of the motives behind the search for extraterrestrial intelligence?

_____

_____

_____

_____

Science Gazette: Futures in Science

Exploring the Universe

Voyage to the Red Planet
Science Reading Skill: Finding the Main Idea

In writing, an author tries to convey a certain idea to the reader. The reader must grasp this main idea in order to understand what the author is saying. If you understand the main idea of several paragraphs, you should be able to grasp the main idea of the entire article. To find the main idea, a helpful technique is to ask yourself two questions. What is the topic of the paragraph? What does the author want me to know about this topic? The answer to the first question will tell you what the paragraph is about. The answer to the second question will put together all the facts about the topic that are presented in the paragraph.

The following paragraph illustrates how the "two-question technique" works.

Winners of the World Series games cannot always be predicted. The best teams from the National League and the American League are pitted against each other. The American League team may have higher batting averages and better outfielders. The National League team may be better in pitching and base running. Which team will become the new world champions?

Topic?   World Series predictions

Main Idea? It is difficult to predict the winners of the World Series.

For each of the following numbered paragraphs in this article, write the topic. Then write the main idea, using your own words, on the lines provided.

Paragraph 4   **Topic?** _____
                   Main Idea? _____

                   _____

Paragraph 5   **Topic?** _____
                   Main Idea? _____

                   _____

Paragraph 6   **Topic?** _____
                   Main Idea? _____

                   _____

Paragraph 13 Topic? _____

Main Idea? _____

_____

Science Reading Skill: Supporting Details

A paragraph would have no meaning without details to support the main idea. Just as a computer needs assistance from a program and the necessary data, so the main idea in a paragraph needs assistance—the supporting details—to make it meaningful.

Listed below are sentences containing the main idea of paragraphs that have been selected from this article. Under each of the main ideas write the details that are directly related to and that support the paragraph's main idea. Refer back to the article in answering these questions.

Paragraph 1
Main Idea: The *Martian Mayflower* explorers show evidence of space fatigue 33 days from Earth.

Supporting Details: _____

_____

_____

_____

_____

Paragraph 13
Main Idea: Giant mirrors in orbit around Mars make it possible for life to exist on Mars.

Supporting Details: _____

_____

_____

_____

Paragraph 16
Main Idea: Voyagers will improve their living conditions on Mars.

Supporting Details: _____

_____

_____

_____

Answer Key

Adventures in Science

Defining Technical Terms Part A 1. large group of stars   **2.** scientists who study planets, stars, and other objects in space **3.** a star that shows a very great increase in brightness and then explodes, releasing matter and energy   **4.** substance of which anything is made   **5.** join together **6.** substances that cannot ordinarily be broken down into simpler substances **7.** substance in blood that carries oxygen **Part B** Sentences will vary.   **Sequence of Events 1.** d   **2.** e   **3.** a   **4.** b   **5.** c

Issues in Science

Previewing (**Note:** *Students should do this activity before reading the article.*) c **Reading Comprehension 1.** The article discusses the disagreement among scientists as to the possible existence of intelligent life elsewhere in the universe.   **2.** This planet is the home of intelligent life.   **3.** They say that "rare accidents" led to the evolution of intelligent life on Earth. The odds are against the same events occurring anywhere else in the universe.   **4.** Even though scientists have not yet found evidence of the existence of intelligent life elsewhere in the universe, it does not necessarily mean that such life does not exist.   **5.** Morrison suggested that scientists listen for radio signals at the "magic frequency" of 1420 megahertz—the frequency of hydrogen.   **6.** Answers will vary. Some people believe it would be a comfort to know we are not alone in the universe. The whole universe could be regarded as our home. We would realize that everyone must live together cooperatively.

Futures in Science

Finding the Main Idea   Paragraph 4 Topic: planet Mars   **Main Idea:** The people of the *Martian Mayflower* had some knowledge of Mars.   **Paragraph 5 Topic:** robot vehicles and instruments   **Main Idea:** Robots could make the difference between life and death for the settlers on Mars.   **Paragraph 6 Topic:** landing site for the *Martian Mayflower*   **Main Idea:** A plateau was selected as the ideal place for the spaceship touchdown.   **Paragraph 13 Topic:** giant mirrors orbiting around Mars   **Main Idea:** Giant mirrors in orbit around Mars make it possible for life to exist there.   **Supporting Details   Paragraph 1:** Some are angry and hostile. Most settlers have headaches and nausea. Some are depressed and withdrawn. Most settlers are tense and weary.   **Paragraph 13:** Microwaves beamed by the mirrors to a power station on Mars are converted to electricity. Electricity is used in the life support systems. Carbon dioxide is liquefied and removed, creating a breathable mixture of gases.   **Paragraph 16:** They collect instruments and materials from other craft. They will use these things to create better living conditions.

Activity Bank

TO THE TEACHER

One of the most exciting and enjoyable ways for students to learn science is for them to experience it firsthand—to be active participants in the investigative process. Throughout the *Prentice Hall Science* program, ample opportunity has been provided for hands-on, discovery learning. With the inclusion of the Activity Bank in this Activity Book, students have additional opportunities to hypothesize, experiment, observe, analyze, conclude, and apply—all in a nonthreatening setting using a variety of easily obtainable materials.

These highly visual activities have been designed to meet a number of common classroom situations. They accommodate a wide range of student abilities and interests. They reinforce and extend a variety of science skills and encourage problem solving, critical thinking, and discovery learning. The required materials make the activities easy to use in the classroom or at home. The design and simplicity of the activities make them particularly appropriate for ESL students. And finally, the format lends itself to use in cooperative-learning settings. Indeed, many of the activities identify a cooperative-learning strategy.

Students will find the activities that follow exciting, interesting, entertaining, and relevant to the science concepts being learned and to their daily lives. They will find themselves detectives, observing and exploring a range of scientific phenomena. As they sort through information in search of answers, they will be reminded to keep an open mind, ask lots of questions, and most importantly, have fun learning science.

Contents

Activity

All the Colors of the Rainbow

Stars come in many different colors—from blue stars, to yellow stars such as the sun, all the way to red stars at the opposite end of the spectrum. The visible light emitted by stars is also made up of different colors. To study starlight, astronomers use a spectroscope. A spectroscope breaks up light into its characteristic colors. In this activity you will build a simple spectroscope.

Materials
shoe box
scissors
cardboard
tape
diffraction grating
black construction paper
uncoated light bulb

Procedure
1. Carefully cut two small, square holes in opposite ends of a shoe box.
2. Tape two small pieces of cardboard on either side of one hole to make a narrow slit.

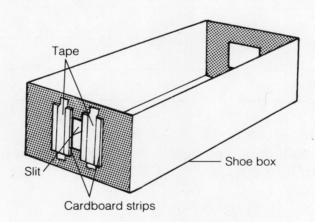

Tape

Slit

Cardboard strips

Shoe box

3. Tape a piece of diffraction grating over the other hole. **Note:** *Before you tape the diffraction grating in place, hold it up in front of a light. Turn the diffraction grating so that the light spreads out into a horizontal spectrum.*

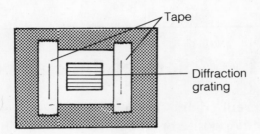

4. Cover the inside of the shoe box, except for the two holes, with black construction paper. Then tape the shoe box closed.

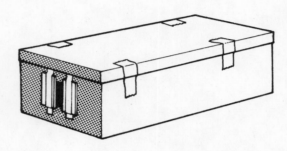

5. Hold your spectroscope so that the slit is parallel to the bright filament of an uncoated light bulb. Look at the light and describe what you see. **CAUTION:** *Do not point your spectroscope at the sun. Never look directly at the sun.*

_____

_____

_____

_____

Going Further

If a fluorescent light bulb or a neon light is available, look at it through your spectroscope and describe its spectrum.

Activity

Swing Your Partner

Gravity is the force of attraction between all objects in the universe. The more mass an object has, the stronger its gravitational attraction. The Earth has the largest mass of any nearby object, so we are always aware of the Earth's gravity. On Earth, gravity keeps our feet firmly on the ground! Gravity also causes falling bodies to accelerate, or change their velocity, as they fall toward the Earth's surface. The acceleration caused by the Earth's gravity is equal to 1 g. In this activity you will measure the value of g in meters per second per second (m/sec^2).

Materials
string
metric ruler
eraser
ring stand
clock or watch with second hand

Procedure
1. Tie an eraser to a piece of string about 50 cm long.

2. Make a pendulum by tying the free end of the string to the arm of a ring stand. Record the length of the string, in meters, in the Data Table on page 92.

3. Pull the eraser to one side and release it. Count the number of complete swings the eraser makes in 60 sec. Record this number in the Data Table.

4. Use the following equation to find the period (T) of the pendulum:

$$T = 60 \text{ sec/number of swings}$$

Record the period, in seconds, in the Data Table.

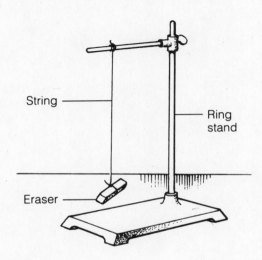

String

Ring stand

Eraser

5. Repeat steps 3 and 4 three more times. Find the average period of the pendulum.

6. Calculate the gravitational acceleration *g* using the following formula:

$$g = 4\pi^2 L/T^2$$

In this formula, $\pi = 3.14$, *L* is the length of the pendulum in meters, and *T* is the average period of the pendulum in seconds. What value did you find for *g*?

Observations

DATA TABLE

Trial	Length (m)	Time (sec)	Number of Swings	Period (sec)
1		60		
2		60		
3		60		
4		60		

Think for Yourself

You may have heard astronauts refer to the "gee forces" they experienced during lift-off. What do you think they were referring to?

Activity

How Can You Observe the Sun Safely?

As you know, it is extremely dangerous to look directly at the sun. Viewing the sun directly can result in permanent damage to your eyes. Is there a safe way to observe the sun? The answer is yes. The best way of looking at the sun is to project an image of the sun onto a piece of white paper. You can demonstrate this by making a simple pinhole viewer. You will need a shoe box, a white index card, tape, and a pin.

1. Tape the index card to the inside of one end of the shoe box. Use a pin to make a small hole in the opposite end of the shoe box. In a darkened room, hold the shoe box so that sunlight enters the pinhole. You should see an image of the sun projected onto the index card. Describe what you see.

_____

_____

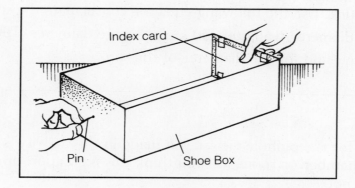

With a little simple mathematics, you can use a similar setup to measure the diameter of the sun. You will need a meterstick, two index cards, tape, and a pin.

2. Tape an index card to one end of the meterstick to make a screen. Make a pinhole in the other index card and hold it at the opposite end of the meterstick. Sunlight passing through the pinhole will form an image of the sun on the screen. Measure the diameter, in centimeters, of the sun's image on the screen. What is the diameter of the image?

_____

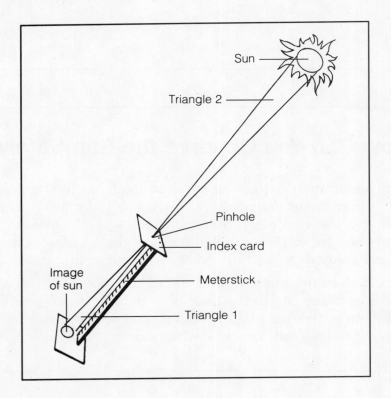

As you can see in the diagram, light rays passing through the pinhole to form the image make two similar triangles. This means that the ratio of the sun's diameter to its distance from the pinhole is the same as the ratio of the diameter of the image to the length of the meterstick. Use the following equation to calculate the sun's diameter:

Sun's diameter/150,000,000 km = Image diameter/100 cm

What value did you find for the diameter of the sun?

_____

Think for Yourself

The Latin name for the pinhole viewer you made in this activity is *camera obscura,* which means dark chamber or room. Do you think this is an appropriate name for this device? Why or why not?

_____

_____

_____

Activity —————————————————————— **The Solar System**

Rusty Nails

Mars is often called the Red Planet. The surface of Mars appears red because the soil contains iron oxide—more commonly known as rust. You are probably familiar with rust closer to home. Anything made of iron that is exposed to air and moisture will become rusted. Junked cars, iron fences, and old bicycles are all subject to rusting. Is there any way to prevent objects from rusting? In this activity you will explore some ways to prevent rusting.

Materials
3 iron nails
clear nail polish
petroleum jelly
glass jar
vinegar

Procedure
1. Coat one of the nails with clear nail polish. Coat the second nail with petroleum jelly. Do not put anything on the third nail.
2. Place the nails into a jar of water. Add some vinegar to the water to speed up the rusting process.

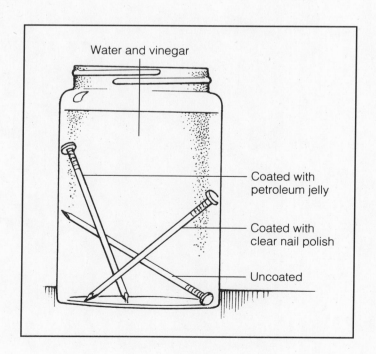

Water and vinegar

Coated with petroleum jelly

Coated with clear nail polish

Uncoated

3. Allow the nails to stand in the glass jar overnight. Then examine the nails. Which nail shows signs of rusting? How do you think the nail polish and petroleum jelly prevented the nails from rusting?

_____

_____

_____

Going Further

What are some other substances that would prevent the nails from rusting? Repeat this experiment to test your ideas.

Do It Yourself

Rusting can cause a great deal of damage to bridges and other objects made of iron by wearing away the metal. Rusty objects can also be dangerous to your health. If you accidentally cut yourself on a rusty nail or other sharp object, you should see a doctor immediately. Using first-aid books or other reference materials, find out why cuts caused by rusty objects are so dangerous.

Action, Reaction

According to Newton's third law of motion, every action causes an equal and opposite reaction. This is the principle of reaction engines, such as rockets. It is also the principle that may cause you to get soaked if you try jumping from a small boat onto the dock! Here's a simple experiment you can perform to demonstrate Newton's third law of motion for yourself.

Materials
skateboard
cardboard strip, 15 cm x 75 cm
windup toy car

Procedure
1. Place the skateboard upside down on the floor.

2. Place the strip of cardboard on top of the wheels of the skateboard. The cardboard will be the "road" for the toy car.

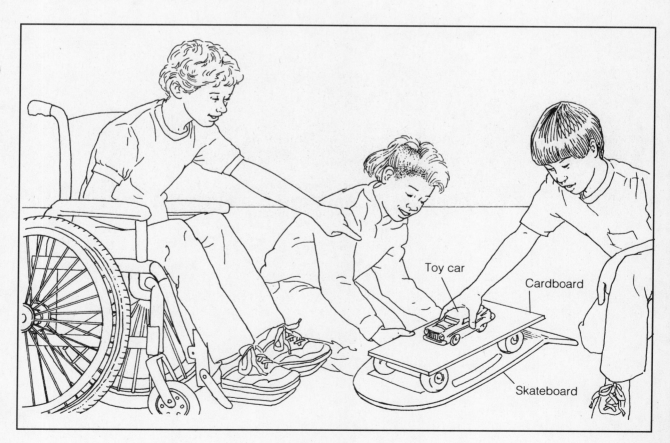

3. Place the toy car on the cardboard, wind it up, and let it go. Observe what happens. Does the car or the road move?

_____

Think for Yourself

1. Are you aware of the road moving away from you when you are driving in a real car? Why or why not?

_____

_____

_____

2. Would you be able to drive a car forward if you were not "attached" to the Earth? Why or why not?

_____

_____

_____

Activity

Earth and Its Moon

What Causes High Tides?

The rise and fall of Earth's oceans—the tides—are caused by the pull of the moon's gravity on the Earth. Because the moon exerts different gravitational forces on different parts of the Earth, there are two high tides and two low tides every day at any given place. You can demonstrate the forces that cause the tides in this activity.

Materials
construction paper
tape
drawing compass
3 equal masses
3 springs

Procedure
1. Tape a piece of construction paper onto a smooth, flat surface. Using the compass, draw a circle 30 cm in diameter on the construction paper.
2. Label the three masses A, B, and C.
3. Attach the springs to the three masses as shown in the diagram. Place mass B in the center of the circle. The circle represents the Earth.

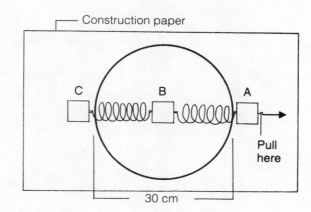

4. Apply a force to mass A by pulling on the spring. This force represents the gravitational pull of the moon on the Earth.

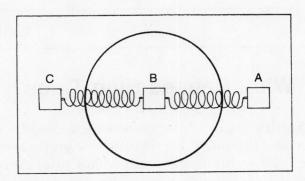

Analysis and Conclusions

1. What happens to the other two masses when you exert a force on mass A?

_____

_____

_____

_____

2. How does this demonstration illustrate the two high tides on opposite sides of the Earth caused by the pull of the moon?

_____

_____

_____

_____

Answer Key

Activity: All the Colors of the Rainbow

Teacher's Note The spectrum of a fluorescent light bulb includes the bright violet, green, and yellow lines emitted by mercury vapor inside the bulb. The neon gas in a neon light glows bright red.

5. Students should be able to see a spectrum containing all the colors of the rainbow on either side of the slit.

Activity: Swing Your Partner

6. The gravitational acceleration g is equal to 9.8 m/sec². **Think for Yourself** The term "gee" forces, or g forces, refers to the downward force felt by the astronauts caused by the upward acceleration of the launch vehicle during liftoff. For example, the acceleration of 4 g's felt by astronauts on liftoff is equal to a force of 39.2 m/sec² (4 × 9.8 m/sec²).

Activity: How Can You Observe the Sun Safely?

1. Descriptions will vary. **2.** The diameter of the sun's image should be about 0.9 cm. The diameter of the sun is 1,350,000 km. **Think for Yourself** Answers will vary. Thousands of years ago, the Arabs and Chinese built full-sized darkened rooms in which people could stand and view scenes from outside. Students may suggest that the inside of the pinhole viewer is similar to such a "dark room."

Activity: Rusty Nails

Teacher's Note A layer of paint or oil will also prevent the nails from rusting. **3.** The uncoated nail shows signs of rusting. Nail polish and petroleum jelly form a protective layer that prevents the iron from coming into contact with the water. **Do It Yourself** Dangerous tetanus bacteria may be present on rusty objects. If you are cut with a rusty metal object, you should get a tetanus shot immediately if you have not had a tetanus vaccination within the past 10 years.

Activity: Action, Reaction

3. The road moves. **Think for Yourself** You are not normally aware of the road moving away from you when you are driving in a real car because the Earth is much larger than the car, making its motion unobservable compared to the car's motion. A car would not be able to move forward if it were not "attached" to the Earth, because the wheels would have nothing to push against.

Activity: What Causes High Tides?

Analysis and Conclusions As a force is applied to mass A, it is accelerated to the right. This stretches the spring and creates a smaller acceleration of mass B and a still smaller acceleration of mass C. The result is a separation of mass A from mass B and of mass B from mass C. In the same way, the ocean facing the moon is pulled away from the Earth, and the Earth is pulled away from the water facing away from the moon. The result is two bulges, or high tides, on opposite sides of the Earth.

MAKING PUPPETS THE "FAIRYLAND WAY"

Making Puppets the "Fairyland Way"

BY

Randal J. Metz

Photographs By

Carl LaRue

Patterns By
Marian Derby,
Lewis Mahlmann,
and Lettie C. Schubert

Charlemagne Press
Garden Bay, BC, Canada

Making Puppets the "Fairyland Way"

Library and Archives Canada Cataloguing in Publication

Metz, Randal J. (Randal John), 1959-
    Making puppets the "fairyland way" / by Randal J. Metz ;
photographs
by Carl LaRue.

Includes bibliographical references.
ISBN 978-0-921845-37-9

    1. Puppet making. I. LaRue, Carl, 1964- II. Title.

TT174.7.M48 2012   745.592'24   C2012-901535-0

ISBN-13: 978-0-921845-37-9

Charlemagne Press
4348 Coastview Drive
Garden Bay, BC
V0N 1S1, Canada
http://charlemagnepress.com

Table of Contents

PREFACE

Children's Fairyland. What memories those two words awaken in the hearts of millions of children and once-upon-a-time children. And a major component of those memories is the park's Storybook Puppet Theater.

The theater played an important role in my early career. Appointed the theater's director at the age of twenty, I was following directly in the footsteps of the incredibly talented Tony Urbano. To further complicate matters, I was also a full-time student at San Francisco State.

At that time the contract required a minimum of five new productions during the park's nine-month season. (I did six - adding a musical review to close each season.) With so little time to create each new show, I relied on the types 'A' and 'B' heads which Randal has so clearly detailed in this book. The patterns, developed by three members of the San Francisco Bay Area Puppeteers Guild, are extremely versatile and can be used create an unlimited cast of characters. They are easy to use and can even be modified for special needs.

So pull out the felt and raid the costume fabric stash. Have fun and see where your imagination leads.

Oh yes, another reason the Storybook Puppet Theater is so special - I met Arlyn, my talented late wife, at the stage door.

Luman Coad, Coad Canada Puppets
Garden Bay, BC
March, 2012

INTRODUCTION

Wanna make a puppet? This book will guide you, for this is how
we make many of the puppets at the Storybook Puppet Theater at
Children's Fairyland in Oakland, California.

Here are directions, patterns, and photos to help you find your way
into the puppet world. You'll have fun if you follow the directions
as described. The patterns are tried and true - all you need is cotton
cloth and felt...or some other wonderful fabric you might find.

No need of paint, paper-maché or and other "gooey" stuff! A
sewing machine is a big help. A bit of bendable cardboard...yarn for
hair...masking tape and buttons for eyes, combine to help you make
many beautiful puppets ready for performance

Lewis Mahlmann

CHAPTER 1: THE MAGIC OF THE STORYBOOK PUPPET THEATER

Snuggled on the banks of Lake Merritt, in Oakland's Lakeside Park, is Children's Fairyland. Opened in 1950, pre-Disneyland, Fairyland has always been an enchanted playground where children's literature can come to life. This happens in various forms: storybook structures for climbing and playing, audio tales for the young ones to listen to, plays presented by child actors, and of course the most popular, the Storybook Puppet Theater.

Fig #1: The Children's Fairyland Storybook Puppet Theater.

The theater, created to look like the open pages of a child's book, has become the longest, ongoing professional puppet theater in the United States. Fifty-five plus years of quality family puppet presentations. The puppets perform seven different tales a year, ranging in style from popular stories to cultural fables and tales, to classic novels and even as far as interpreting ballets, operas and classical musical pieces. All done with puppets and geared for young children.

Fig. #2: Children's Fairyland's Puppet Theatre ad designed by Sheilah Beckett, a Golden Book illustrator.

Since its inception, Fairyland has realized puppets are a viable way of teaching children literary tales, morals, and of presenting entertainment in a unique way enjoyed by the entire family.

Children's Fairyland was created with the concept that young children need an amusement park designed to not be over stimulating. To this effect, almost all the park structures are constructed to be "child size." Adults must stoop to enter this small world which is played in by their thrilled little ones. Fairytale settings, the surrounding flora and fauna, and even the live animals exhibited at the park blend together to create this world which is "just right" for a small child. Everything is exactly the right size for toddlers. Especially the puppets.

All of the parks play sets spring from the pages of popular children's tales. Children can play on Captain Hook's pirate ship, become lost in Alice's Wonderland Tunnel, or visit the homes of many famous nursery rhyme characters. And these play structures often feature figurative statues of the tale's characters they represent. Literacy is first and foremost in the minds of the Fairyland staff. Which is why the puppet theater, opened in 1956, is built in the shape of a giant open storybook with the puppet proscenium placed proudly in the center of the book.

Fig #3: Storybook Puppet Theater model created by William Russell Everritt, designer of Children's Fairyland.

The theater was designed by San Francisco bohemian architect William Russell Everritt, with input from Bay Area puppeteers such as Lettie Connell Schubert and Ralph Chessé. So from the start, the building was "puppet friendly" to performing puppeteers. Over the years, the theater has had five prominent puppet directors. Each raising the bar higher on the puppet playing field. Frank and Dorothy Hayward were the first directors, bringing their hand carved marionettes to perform for the kids. They loved "old world" craftsmanship. In the beginning, the director was responsible for producing five puppet productions a year.

Fig #4: The Hayward Marionettes: Clifford Coite, Dorothy and Frank Hayward, and Beverly Philis present *"Hansel & Gretel"*.

After the Haywards, Tony Urbano took over the controls (pardon the pun) of the marionette theater. His puppets were cast and made of celastic, and featured animated mouths and eyes. Most of his marionettes had special strings and workings. Soon, Tony left Fairyland to create puppets for films and commercials in the Los Angeles area.

Fig. #5: Tony Urbano Marionettes present *"Hansel & Gretel"* (left) and *"Little Red Riding Hood"* (right).

Our next puppeteer was Luman Coad. After leaving a sister amusement park, he settled amongst the pages of the Storybook Theater. Luman specialized in creating his own tales, with puppets which were often sculpted out of felts and stuffed with cotton - much like the patterns in this book. Luman left Fairyland and moved to Canada, where he created the internationally known Coad Canada Puppets with his wife Arlyn. At Fairyland Luman presented six different puppet tales a year.

Fig. #6: Luman Coad presents *"Wilbur, the Dragon"* (left) and *"The Blue Willow Plate"* (right).

After Luman, Lewis Mahlmann became our resident puppet director for the next twenty-three years. The Fairyland Trustees now decided the puppet theater should increase its number of performances to seven shows a year! That's a lot of puppets to make in order to fill the obligation. To this end, Lewis collaborated with Bay Area puppeteers Lettie Schubert and Marian Derby to create the hand puppet patterns you are about to learn how to use. They allowed us to make fast, durable puppets to use in some of our tales, while other puppet presentations enlisted figures which were carved or sculpted and took longer to produce.

Lewis Mahlmann is well known for his adaptations of classic ballets and operas for puppets as well as his renditions of cultural tales from around the world. He and his partner, David Cadwalader Jones, have written four books of puppet plays, presented at Fairyland, and are available for use in schools and recreation programs.

Fig #7: Lewis Mahlmann productions of *"The Little Dipper"* (lelt)& *"Beauty and the Beast"* (right).

In 1990, Lewis and his long time apprentice, Randal Metz became co-directors of the theater. Still producing seven shows a year, they ultimately created over 150 productions. Randal is now the sole director and still favors using these puppet patterns to create the park productions as well as for his shows which are traveled to West Coast libraries and fairs under his other puppet identity as *The Puppet Company.*

Fig. #8: Randal Metz presents *"Another Princess & the Pea"* (left) and *"An Irish Tale"* (right)

The patterns in this book have been improved again and again over the years. They are great to use because they do not require extensive casting or sculpting, or carving puppet parts. Just cut all the pieces out of the chosen fabrics and begin stitching! We will also show how to use simple patterns to make wigs, manufacture facial features, and finally costume the characters. Imagination is the only limit. As a bonus, each step is illustrated by photo demonstrations.

These paper patterns have been used all over the country by many famous puppeteers as well. But they were cultivated here in the San Francisco Bay Area and at Children's Fairyland. Let me take a moment to introduce the three talented pros who came up with these great designs.

The idea sprang from the clever mind of Marian Derby. Mrs. Derby was a puppeteer, teacher, and very active in her children's social organizations. Her puppet company, *Party Puppets*, entertained throughout the Bay Area. Although she presented herself as an amateur puppeteer, her results were very professional. Little is left in our archives about her puppet life. We do know she worked extensively with puppeteer and prominent Bay Area art teacher Benjamin Blake. Always interested in the next best way to express herself, Marian moved from puppets into theological studies. She sold some of her shows to Fairyland, and moved away from the "puppet scene." It is from Marian's basic hand puppet body pattern that further puppet parts were conceived. Ms. Derby favored her own papier-maché sculpted heads over the stuffed head patterns in this book.

Fig #9: Marion Derby's *"Punch and Judy."*

Lewis Mahlmann, our second pattern collaborator, has been a professional puppeteer since the late 1950's. As a young man, he studied acting, piano, and singing, which he always brought to his puppet shows. Twice President of the Puppeteers of America, Lewis has also taught puppetry at San Francisco State University, and has co-written several books of puppet plays. Lewis also favors these puppet designs because they give a "toy like" quality to the finished puppets which appeals to small children. Little wonder he loves this look, since his puppet mentor was none other than Burr Tilstrom of *Kukla, Fran & Ollie* fame. Besides his well known work at the Fairyland puppet theater, Lewis also took time to build adult shows, usually classical theatrical pieces, which were produced under his second company name, the *Lilliputian Players*.

Fig #10: Lewis Mahlmann and puppet friend.

Last, but not least, came the improvements suggested by Lettie Connell Schubert. Lettie cut her teeth on the strings of television puppetry in the 1950's. She worked extensively with her mentor, Ralph Chessé on the set of the *Brother Buzz* television show and then behind the scenes on *Looking Glass Lady*. KPIX and KRON channels respectively. Lettie was most known for her simple stylized puppets and her clever manipulation. She has left behind a must-have book for all puppeteers, *A Manual of Hand Puppet Manipulation*. Lettie also managed for five years the well known recreation puppet program in Oakland, the *Vagabond Puppets*. Amongst her many puppet apprentices were teen puppeteers Frank Oz and Jerry Juhl of *Muppet* fame. A wonderful and giving person, Lettie often sought out young talent and then cultivated their successful careers.

Fig. #11: Lettie Connell Schubert with Cuthburt Bunny on the TV set of *"Looking Glass Lady."*

And now we're ready to begin. Just follow the instructions given at each stage of the puppet construction to make puppets like the professionals!

Just for fun, we've included some press photos of Fairyland shows which have used the patterns included in this book. Enjoy.

Fig. #12: *"The Wind in the Willows."*

Fig. #13: *"The Rabbit Who Wanted Red Wings."*

Fig. #14: *"Goldilocks and the Three Bears."*

Fig. #15: *"Raggedy Ann & Andy and the Camel with Wrinkley Knees."*

Fig. #16: *"Aesop's Fables."*

Fig. #17: *"The Magic Mushrooms."*

Fig. #18: *"The Pied Piper."*

Fig. #19: *"The Enchanted Well."*

Fig. #20: *"Orca, the First Whale."*

Fig. #21: *"Peter and the Wolf."*

Fig. #22: *"Trickster Tales."*

Fig. #23: *"Alice in Wonderland."*

Photos in this chapter are courtesy of Children's Fairyland archives.

Chapter 2: Using Our Hand Puppet Patterns

The hand puppet is a very special type of creature. Through the use of hand & muscle reflexes, the puppeteer is able to breathe life into the inanimate figure. At Fairyland, we use hand puppets for shows where the characters need to convey a lot of feelings, or must move with grace and/or precision. The marionette or rod puppet does not have the same performance style as the hand puppet. Each is chosen for different reasons, as we will discuss when the time comes. The hand puppet focuses on hand, head and waist movements so less costuming or binding material is always a plus.

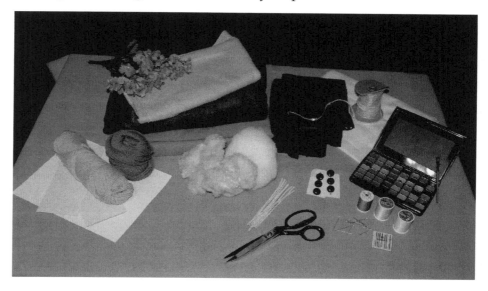

Fig #1: Some of the suggested materials ready for construction.

Below is a compiled, suggested list of items needed for making a hand puppet:

1) Felt or fleece colors for the hands and head
2) Unbleached muslin for the body sleeve
3) Suitable fabrics and trims for the costume
4) Threads: sewing and/or embroidery for the above materials

5) Stuffing for the head and body parts.
6) Yarns or furs for wigs
7) Faceted buttons for the eyes
8) Small make up selection of eye shadows for face details
9) Bendable, thin cardboard for the neck and wig templates.
10) Pipe cleaner for fingers of the hands
11) Water color sketch pad and paints for design work
12) Sand for filling the legs & shoes

And of course....scissors, pins, needles, masking tape, marking pens, and paper for extra patterns (as needed).

And most important of all......a dependable sewing machine!

Having all supplies ready and close at hand always makes for a smooth construction process. It also shows thought has been given to the character, and it eliminates any extra trips to get supplies during a moment of inspiration.

DESIGNING THE PUPPET

Before cutting fabrics for any puppet, we suggest first creating a watercolor sketch of the figure. This clarifies how the puppet should look and acts as a guide during construction. Watercolor is easy to use and lends itself to "happy accidents" while mixing colors and smoothing line work. Remember it's easier to make changes on paper rather than after cutting and sewing.

Fig #2: Designing the puppet.

On costume design, Lewis Mahlmann suggests:

"*You should sketch out your puppet designs first so that you have color harmony in your final production. Helping to identify the various puppet characters and intensifying the scenic effect are the main reasons for designing costumes. You can help the personality of a puppet with its costume and point up the puppet's action too. Think of the costume design to be part of the total scenic effect. Build a puppet's costume as you would sculpture, only instead of plaster or paper-maché you are working with all kinds of fabrics. Costumes should be designed to illustrate the character of the puppet in the show but at the same time have a relation with the rest of the costumes of the other puppets and the accompanying scenery. Remember all the textures, as well as colors, available to you. In any costume, period or otherwise, understand the designs that you look up in picture or reference books. Get the essential feeling of the style, the general effect. When a costume gets too busy, nothing is seen. Keep your design simple and you can't go wrong.*"

Fig. #3: Finished watercolor design.
(Color photo on back cover.)

For this puppet example we have chosen the popular character of an elf or "Puck." Let's begin bringing this woodland creature to life. Have fun, and don't be afraid to experiment or add your own touches as we proceed.

In preparing to use these patterns, we suggest photocopying them from the book or tracing them onto paper then cutting out the pieces of the copied patterns. That way, the master patterns will remain intact in the book.

STYLE 'A' HEAD

Step 1 - Cutting out the head pieces using the Male or Female head patterns. Head style 'A'.

Select the head pattern pieces to be used and trace them onto the backside of the material chosen for the head and hands. (see Fig #4) Remember to waste as little of the fabric as possible and to have the patterns running the same direction on the fabric bias. When finished there should be two (2) profile head pieces, one (1) of the head insert for the 'A' head, and one (1) of the chin insert - a total of four (4) pieces.

Notes:
> • To cut the two identical profile pieces, draw once and fold over the fabric, then cut the two fabric layers.
> • It is always good to have two pairs of scissors on hand. One for cutting paper, and the other for fabric only.

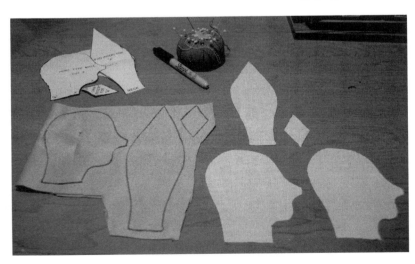

Fig #4: Example of cut out paper pattern pieces (top), drawn on fabric (left), and cut out fabric pieces (right).

Step 2 & 3 - Lining up the patterns properly for sewing.

Place the head insert next to one of the profiles and pin from the neck up. (See Fig #5) With an approximately 1/8″ seam allowance, stitch from the neck all the way up to the point of the head insert. Then pin and stitch opposite profile to the insert and stitch from the point to the neck - joining the three sections together. Next sew the two profile pieces together from the point of the head insert, down the front of the face to the bottom of nose (See Fig #6)

Fig. #5: Pin one side of the head profile to the head insert, with the point at the forehead.

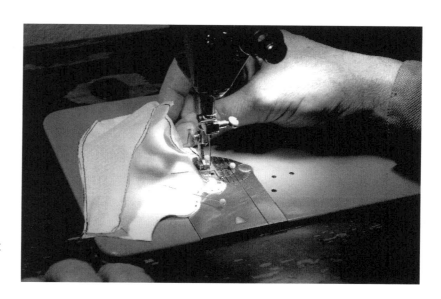

Fig. #6: Three pieces sewn together, continuing from the insert point to the bottom of the nose.

Step 4 - Insertion of the chin pattern.

Pin and sew the small diamond shaped chin insert, with the X point up, to one side of the profile piece from the bottom point to top point of the diamond. Next sew the other side of the diamond from top to bottom, to complete the head. (See Fig #7) Turn the sewn head inside out, push out the chin and nose sections, and check for weak seams. Hand sew if needed. For practice, try sewing both the Male and Female head patterns. The Female head also uses the chin insert.

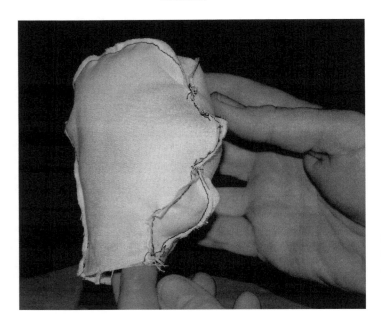

Fig #7: This is what the head looks like with the chin insert sewn in place. The head is ready to be turned inside out.

Step 5- Creating a cardboard neck.

Next prepare a neck tube by cutting a piece of rectangular cardboard (The kind used to send 8 x 10 photos in the mail) about 3 x 4 inches. Roll it around your finger loosely, deciding whether one or two fingers will be used in the neck, and secure with masking tape. (See Fig #8)

Note: The cardboard should be strong enough to take use, yet light enough to bend easily and be hand sewn at the bottom.

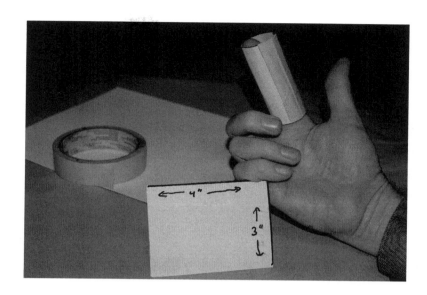

Fig. #8: Neck tube made from cardboard, rolled and taped.

Step 6 - Stuffing the head and sewing in the neck piece.

There are three types of puppet stuffing. The first, and best suited, is kapok. Kapok is an oatmeal colored heavy stuffing material which is most used in the construction of teddy bears. Not every fabric store carries this product, but when found you should probably buy many yards of it. It stuffs solidly and gives great shape to the head. The second choice is white polyester fiber stuffing which is found at all fabric stores, and is great for making pillows. This stuffing is fine to use, but takes more in order to fill out the face and pack properly. The good thing about this stuffing is it makes a lighter head. In some cases this is a plus. The third type of stuffing is for those who like to recycle and make the puppet extremely light: used plastic bags from shops. A great way to save the landfill and try a new product. Choose wisely.

To start, stuff the head until about halfway down. Be sure to carefully stuff the nose of the face. Insert the cardboard neck into the head, all the way in. Stuff the rest of the head, expanding around the cardboard in the middle, and then stuff lightly at the bottom of the neck tube. Be sure to stuff around the neck, the chin, the jaw line and the cheeks. (See Fig #9)

> **Note:** Now is the time to accentuate the face by adding fullness and molding the cheek and chin areas. We often use a thin paint brush handle as a tool while molding and it's good for getting into tight areas.

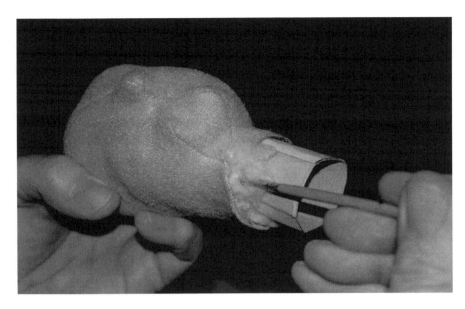

Fig #9: Stuffing the head with the cardboard tube inserted. Notice the paint brush handle used for stuffing and molding kapok into the face.

When the head is stuffed and molded, thread a needle with strong thread and carefully sew the bottom of the neck tube to the fabric neck opening, gathering the fabric as needed. (See Fig #10)

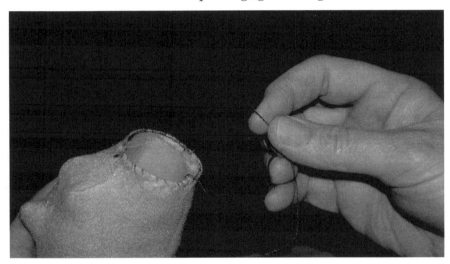

Fig #10: Sewing the neck tube into the head.

Note: For a larger head, feel free to increase the head patterns accordingly an inch or so.

Step 7 - Adding features and "makeup."

Next comes the fun part, creating the puppet character. Before adding nose, eyes and such to a head, I often use what is called "dimpling." That's the use of carpet thread stitched through the head to pull the fabric into shape - such as giving deeper sockets for the eyes, pulling in at the mouth, and giving a stronger jaw line to the figure. I will go into detail about this in Chapter 3. Dimpling can be used with any of these patterns. For this head, I chose to push the chin out by pulling a thread under the chin from cheek to cheek.

On facial design, Lewis Mahlmann suggests:
> "Using your design, plan the features of the face. You might cut the pieces in various colored felts for eyelids, eye backing, and/or mouth. Perhaps the black faceted shiny button eyes can have white or colored felt behind them. You can embroider or glue felt lashes and brows, if so desired, and nostrils too! Remember to keep the face clean and simple."

Cut out a paper pattern for the desired ears. Trace this pattern twice on a folded piece of face fabric and machine sew on the traced lines. Leave an opening at the bottom of the ears. Cut around sewn edges and turn the ears (2) inside out. After turning, machine sew around the ear outline to add extra firmness to the pieces. Lightly trace the eye pattern in place. (see next paragraph) Place the ears on either side of stuffed head, even with the nose, and hand sew on. (See Fig #11) Other ways to make noses will be shown later in this tutorial.

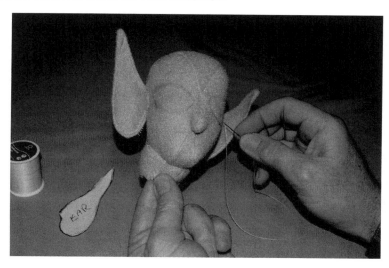

Fig. #11: Notice the eyes lightly traced onto the head. The ears are sewn onto the sides of the head.

The Puck figure will need a white eye fabric behind the button eyes. Cut a paper pattern in the shape of the eye design, keeping in mind the size of the buttons, and cut two (2) out of white felt. Place the felt pieces where the eyes are to be, then hand stitch to the face fabric. Always try to use small stitches. Then sew the button eyes in place over the felt eye piece (See Fig #12) Stitch the buttons into the head from one side of the nose to the other button, pulling the thread a bit to slight indent the eyes. We like to use black, faceted buttons found in most fabric stores. The diamond faceting catches light and gives life to the eyes of the puppet!

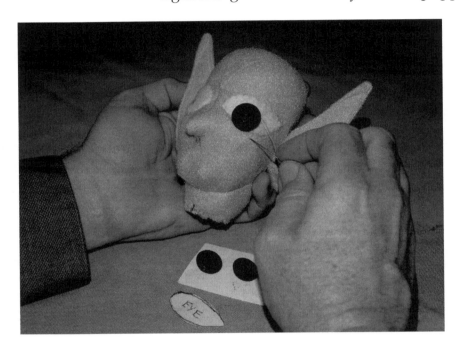

Fig #12: After the white felt backing is sewn in place, sew on the buttons and pull the thread so they focus. **Note:** The paper eye pattern.

Eyelids are easily created by making a half elliptical pattern shape and cutting the two (2) eyelids out of colored felt. These felt pieces are then either hot glued or white glued over the top part of the button eyes. (See Fig #13) A black marking pen can be used to define the eye with a line across the bottom of the felt eyelid.

There are many ways to create mouth details. Lips can be glued-on felt or embroidered. I like to use acrylic paint and hand paint the mouth. I will do so for this puppet. However, colored marking pens give the same quality. (See Fig #14) Another way to achieve a good mouth is to cut a white felt piece for teeth, and then cut top and bottom lips out of two colors of a red felt and glue them over the white felt.

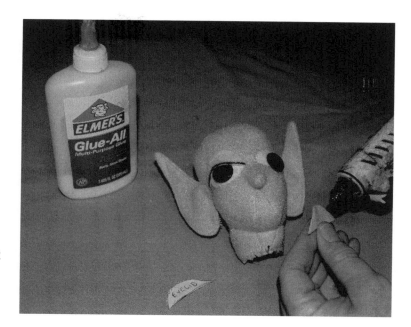

Fig. #13: White glue or hot glue the felt eyelids in place, and draw a black line at the bottom of the lid. See left eye.

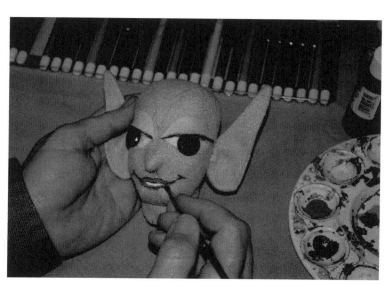

Fig. #14: Colored pens, acrylic paint, or felt can be used to create the puppet's mouth.

And now acrylic paints or colored marking pens can be used to add details such as face lines, wrinkles, eye puckers, and eyebrows. (See Fig #15) I usually take a black pen and draw around the bottom of the eye to the eyelid and then add two (2) laugh creases on the side. Eyebrows are created by making slashing strokes (just like your own eyebrows) above the eyelids. Or by cutting the eyebrows out of felt and gluing them on as well. Embroidering also make a nice eyebrow. Even feathers!

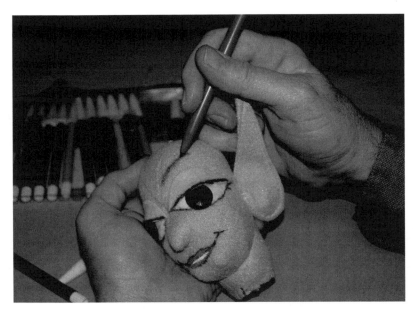

Fig #15: Using pens, add other facial lines at needed. Notice the line under the right eye ending in laugh creases.

At last it's time to use makeup rouge to highlight and shadow the face. For this process, use a dark color for deep shadow and a light reddish color for cheeks and hands. (See Fig #16) The dark color is applied like a woman's makeup. If the eyelids are not cut out of felt, makeup can be used instead. A dark color lightly under the chin will shadow the jaw line. Do not overuse. Use sparingly at first and see if it achieves the desired effect. Reapply if needed. The red rouge color is used to highlight the cheeks for blush, and the forehead, ears and nose for added life. Apply on these places. We also will sometimes lightly apply the blush color over the tops of our puppet hands to bring some life to the felt. (Usually the top knuckles and palm)

Fig #16: Puck's head with makeup applied. Don't worry if the makeup looks too heavy. When the puppet is finished, it won't look so clownish. (Color photo on back cover.)

To keep the makeup color on the face, we lightly spray the face with a matte clear top coat. Test this on a piece of felt with rouge applied before spraying the finished face.

Step 8 - Making a wig.

Many products can be used to make hair for puppets. Hair can be layered fringe, which moves nicely when the puppet nods. Fake fur, feather boa, Brillo pads, or even layered felt are effective. The most common type of puppet hair is made with yarn. This is the material I will show how to use. I will also show some other examples of using yarn to make puppet braids and curls .

Fig. #17: Yarn is available in many thicknesses. Feathers, fringe, fur, and boa make great and easy puppet wigs.

On wig making, Lewis Mahlmann suggests:
> "Using wool rug yarn is best because it has lots of body and will hold up. It isn't as soft as sweater yarn. Think in broad terms for the total effect of the wig. For a neat look, try using two color shades of yarn when you fashion your wig piece."

The first step in wig making is to decide how thick the yarn will be and what colors. (See Fig #17)

Next measure from ear to ear and from the top of the head to the desired length of the hair piece. In the case of our elf, it is 4" x 4 -1/2". As a precaution, I will add another inch to both of those measurements. Cut a piece of cardboard, which is light enough to be sewn on a machine, to the above measurements. Make a slit in the top corner of the cardboard, catch the end of the yarn in the slit, and then wrap the yarn loosely, yet firmly, all the way across the cardboard piece.

Note: You do not need to wrap a lot, since both sides add yarn thickness at the wig. When wrapped, cut the last strand from the yarn skein and get ready to machine sew. Lightly catching the threads above the cardboard, sew across the yarn to create a top seam. (See Fig #18)

Fig #18: Sew across the top of the cardboard, lightly catching the yarn so it will pull freely off the card when finished. Two colors are used on this wig.

There are two different methods of removing the yarn from the cardboard. If the puppet is going to have straight hair, carefully cut across the yarn at the bottom (unsewn) edge of the cardboard. Then pull the seam at the top and the yarn will tear away from the card, while while the stitched line holds the yarn web together. (See Fig #19) To curl up the hair at the base of the neck, do not cut the yarn. Instead, carefully pull the top seam to separate the sewn yarn from the card stock. Then pull the cardboard, from the side, out of the wrapped yarn. (See Fig #20) Run a second seam over the first hair seam to double stitch yarn.

Note: For an example of the second style of hair, look at the finished Round Head in Fig. #30.

Fig. #19: For straight hair, cut the yarn on the unseamed bottom and remove from the card.

Fig. #20 For a curled look at the bottom of the wig, pull top seam away from the card and remove the cardboard from the side.. Notice the notch for holding the end of the yarn at the top right corner.

A simple wig idea to use the stitching at the top of the yarn to create a part running from the top of the head down to the middle of the neck. This gives a neat "long haired" type of look for the puppet. Don't forget to hide the ripped cardboard (if any) under the seam showing on the back. See how it might work with our Puck head! (See Fig #21)

Another great way of adding body to a wig piece is to layer sections of yarn onto the felt head. (See Fig #22) Notice how we can add as many layers needed with this process. For Puck we will just use one layer. As each layer is placed on the head, hand stitch the top of the seamed yarn to the head making sure the hair extends to the sides and in front of ears.

Fig #21: For a "long haired" look, place the yarn with the top seam running from the forehead over the top to the back of the head. Notice the added felt horns.

Fig #22: Place the yarn web across the back as shown and hand stitch the top seam to the head. Then lightly catch the yarn to the back of the head all the way across the lower portion.

The stitched thatch of hair will be longer than needed. Use what is needed for the desired section of wig and cut off the excess. This extra piece can become bangs for the front of the wig. Sew the bang piece, with the loose ends towards the back of the head, on top of the first section. Then flip the bang section forward onto the forehead. The sewn seam is now hidden by the flip! Hand stitch, or glue the yarn on forehead, and cut to the design look. (See Fig #23) This is how we make a simple wig. For a pompadour or upsweep look to the bangs, use the example for hair in Fig #20. Follow the step above, and lightly catch with thread the curled yarn to the puppet's forehead.

Fig. #23 Notice how the seam is hidden by sewing the bangs section to the bottom piece, then pulling it over the forehead. Stitch lightly to the forehead.

Note: A hat, or flowered head gear is always a plus for hiding unwanted seams on finished wigs.

Another fun thing to add to wigs are curls. A simple way to create these is shown below. (See Fig #24) Take a wood dowel, the thickness of the curls, tape the end of the yarn at one end of the dowel, then wrap around the dowel to the desired length. Tape the yarn at bottom to hold in place. Hand stitch up the length of the curl, catching the yarn all the way to the top, then reverse and stitch down the opposite side. When finished sewing, cut off the yarn tail, remove the tapes, and slide the yarn off the dowel. Repeat as needed. Another way to do this is to glue the yarn around the dowel and then cut the dowel to the desired curl lengths when dried. Paint exposed ends of dowels to match wig color, and sew into the wig.

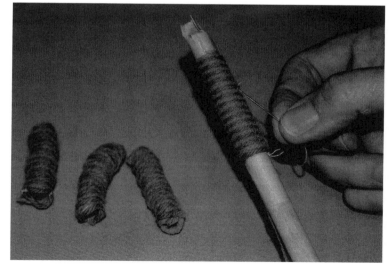

Fig. #24 Make curls by wrapping yarn around a dowel, the hand sewing on both sides to lightly catch the yarn. Remove and spray with a matte coating for strength.

Some hairdos look good with small braids on the sides of the face, or maybe a long braid wrapped around the back of the head. Braids are fun and easy to make. Here's a fast way: hammer two nails partially into a board, separated by slightly more than the length of the intended braid. Tie the end of the yarn onto the top nail then wrap yarn around the nails to get the desired thickness of the braid. (See Fig #25) Cut the yarn at the bottom, braid (See Fig # 26), then stitch the bottom of yarn to hold the braid together and slip it off the top nail. Now see how it can be applied to head. (See Fig #27) As the photo shows, it looks silly on Puck.

Fig #25: Wrap yarn around two nails to create a desired braid's thickness.

Fig #26: Braid then stitch the bottom closed.

Fig. #27 Finished braid as it might look on a head. But we won't use it on Puck.

It's fun to see how many wigs can be made by using all types of products. Experiment and discover. Your imagination is the only limit.

STYLE 'B' OR ROUND HEAD

This is my second favorite head pattern to use. The patterns create a round head which allows great characterization. This head is ideal for plump ladies, fat gentlemen, clowns, etc. It's excellent for funny villains too. The nose, like the ears, is made separately from the head. Usually funny noses are ideal for this type of head. Making a pattern for a round nose is shown in Fig #28.

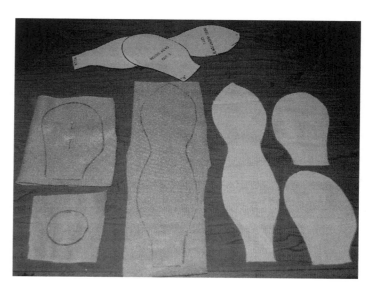

Fig. #28 Style 'B' pattern pieces (top), traced onto fabric (left), and cut out (right.)

Copy head 'B' patterns from the book, cut out the pieces, trace their outlines onto the fabric, and cut out. There should be two (2) profile head pieces, and one (1) head insert for the "B" head.

Note: To cut the two profile pieces needed, draw once and fold the fabric over to cut out two identical sections. (See Fig #27)

Now follow the same procedure used to create the "Hero" or A head. Pin and machine sew a profile piece to the large head insert section. Using an approximate 1/8" seam allowance, start at the back neck and sew all the way around the head to the front of the profile bottom. Then pin and sew, from front to back, the other profile to the insert. Turn inside out, hand sew any weak spots.

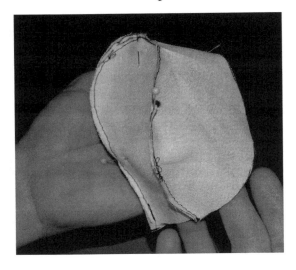

Fig #29: Machine sew the side profile pieces to the head insert at shown.

Fig. #30 Sewn and stuffed style 'B', Round head (left) and how Puck might look (right) with the Round head and different hair style.

When stuffed and with the neck tube sewn in, the head should look like the white Muslin head in Fig #30. For fun, we have created another head for Puck, only this time using the round head, to show how it might look. The round nose on this face was created by cutting a circle of the face material, and stuffing it with while gathering the circle with a running thread. Pull the thread closed, and the material will form a beaded nose for the puppet. Great for lots of characters. We also have changed the hair style on this Puck. Also, the eyes are "dimpled" and the chin is accentuated.

Style 'A' Animal Head

The Animal puppet head we will now create is a horse or a unicorn. Animal heads are made similarly to human heads but without the diamond shaped chin piece. The patterns include an animal head profile, and the head insert for the 'A' style head.

When the animal head pattern is properly traced and cut out, there will be two head pieces and one (1) of the head insert for the 'A' head. (See Fig #31)

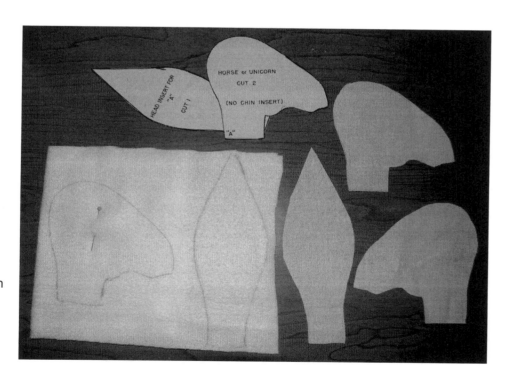

Fig. #31 Horse/Unicorn pattern pieces (top), traced on fabric (left), and cut out (right).

To assemble the Unicorn head, with an approximate 1/8″ seam allowance, pin then sew one profile piece to the head insert. Start at the back of the neck and sew all the way to the point of the insert. The pin and sew the other profile to the insert - starting at the insert point and ending at the neck. Then sew the profile fronts together. Turn the sewn head inside out, check and repair any weak spots, and stuff. (See Fig #32)

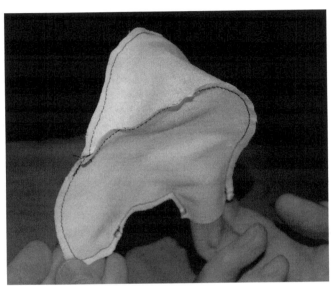

Fig. #32 How the sewn Animal head should look.

When stuffed, and with neck tube sewn in, the head should look like the white Muslin example in Fig #33. We have also created a finished Unicorn face to illustrate how a completed head might look.

Fig. #33 Muslin Animal head (left) and finished Unicorn head (right).

As an bonus to this section, we have included extra animal head patterns created by Lewis Mahlmann. As the years went by, Lewis would often design more and more patterns to be added to these basic patterns. Many have been reprinted in this volume.

About these Animal patterns, Lewis Mahlmann suggests:
"Here are some more animal head patterns you might use. Also included are hand and leg patterns. Use the basic hand puppet pattern sheet and don't forget to put in the top head dart (insert for 'A' head) so that the finished head is wide enough. You will probably have to extend the point of the insert down to the tip of the nose on each animal."

Note: The head insert 'A' must be extended to reach the tip of the nose for each of these animal patterns. Make paper pattern and then mock up each head in muslin first to ensure the desired results.

MAKING THE HAND PUPPET BODY

Step 1 - Creating stuffed hands.

The first step in constructing the puppet's body is to choose a hand pattern which best suits the puppet's design. Although the hand pattern included on our hand puppet sheet is nice, it doesn't have the look we wish for Puck. So I will be using the female hand pattern in "The Fairyland marionette" patterns. This hand type has long, elegant fingers and looks more human. See Chapter 4 for this hand pattern.

Fig. #34 Hand pattern (left) is traced onto the chosen fabric.

Trace the hand pattern twice onto a doubled piece of the flesh material. Do not cut out. (See Fig #34)

Pin the two fabric layers together and machine stitch around the drawn outlines. Rather than a sharp "V" at the base each finger, take three horizontal stitches before continuing up the next finger to ease turning the hand inside out. Be sure to leave the wrist open.

Cut around the outside of the stitching and remove the sewn hand. (See Fig #35)

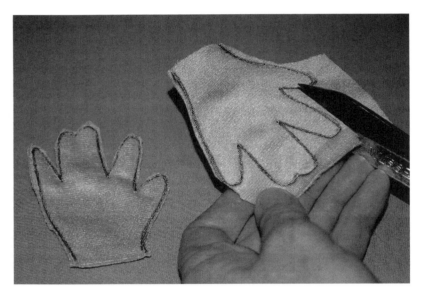

Fig. #35 Cut around sewn hand to remove excess fabric. **Note**: Very carefully cut down into the V section between the finger to avoid cutting the sewn thread.

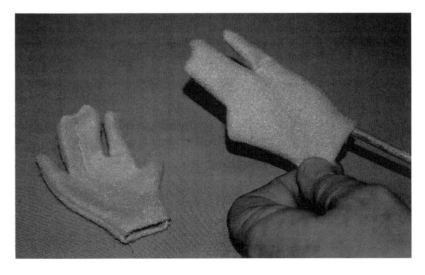

Fig. #36 Reverse the sewn hands as shown. Notice the machine sewn line on the hand at the left, which gives the illusion of two complete fingers.

Carefully reverse the stitched hand, using a paint brush handle
to poke out the fingers. (See Fig #36) Then machine sew down
between the two middle fingers which are joined on the pattern.
(See Fig #36) When stuffed the sewn line will recess and make it
look like there are two fingers.

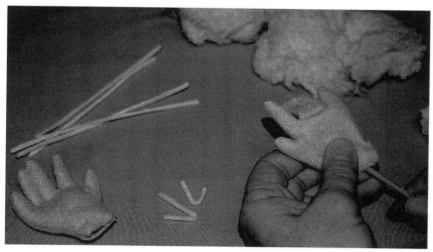

Fig. #37 Insert pipe cleaners
into the fingers for flexibility
then stuff with kapok. Lightly fill
the palm and wrist area.

Before stuffing the hand, cut two "V" shaped pipe cleaners for
each hand. Place one cleaner in the thumb and index finger, and
the other into the index and middle fingers. This will allow the
puppet's fingers to be bent to whatever configuration is needed.
Now stuff the fingers, thumb and lightly fill the palm and wrist
area. (See Fig #37)

Step 2 - Cutting out the basic hand puppet body.

> **Note:** Since the hand/wrist seams take the most pressure
> when working the hand puppet, we have recently adapted
> the pattern to prevent excess wear. The body pattern we use,
> and which is included, has rounded ends to the arms. (See
> Fig #38)

Unbleached Muslin is the best material to use for the hand puppet
body. It is easy to work with, and allows the puppeteer's hand
to slip in and out of the body without difficulty. It also handles
moisture well. Double the unbleached muslin and cut the two, front
and back, body pieces, on the folds of the muslin. (See Figs #39 -
40) The front is narrow and back is almost double the width of the
front. This is because the back of the hand is so much wider than
the distance between the relaxed fingers.

Fig. #38 Hand puppet body pieces cut out and ready for sewing.

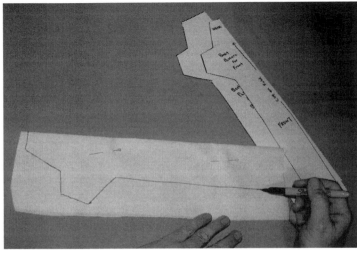

Fig. #39 Hand puppet body patterns (upper right) traced onto muslin. Be sure to align the pattern to the fold of the fabric.

Note: For each section, trace the pattern on the fold of the material to result in a complete body piece.

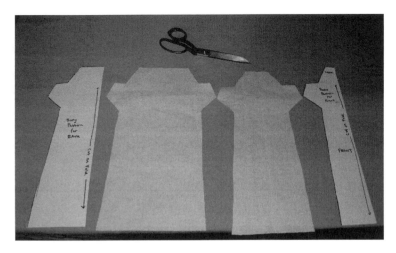

Fig. #40 Hand puppet body pieces cut out and ready to sew. The pattern pieces are on the outside.

Step 3 - Sewing the hand puppet body.

Using a 1/4" seam allowance, machine sew the front section of the body to the back section. (See Fig #40) Always remember to pin each section before sewing. Do *not* turn this piece inside out. Keep the good, finished seam on the inside for comfort. The raw selvages will be hidden by the puppet's costume.

Fig. #41 Sewing front and back sections together.

Steps 4 - 5 - Assembling the body.

Insert the neck of the finished head into the neck opening of the body. Gather the muslin at the neck and sew tightly to the base of the neck. (See Fig #42)

Fig. #42 Sew the body sleeve to the base of the neck. Gather the muslin as needed around the neck line. Notice the adapted body pattern used for this puppet.

Now sew the hands onto the basic body, ensuring the puppeteer's finger will extend into the palm of the hand. When the hand is attached, take another stitch at the base of the thumb and wrap around the hand, circling it a few times and pull. Tie off the stitch. This plumps out the hand and makes it look natural. (See Fig #43)

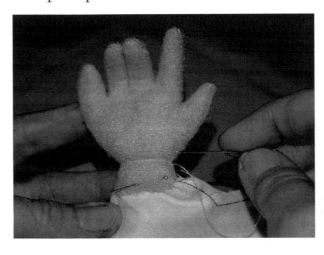

Fig. #43 Sewing the hand onto the body. Notice the thread wrapped around the wrist and pulled to plump out the hand.

COSTUMING A HAND PUPPET

Step 1 - Making puppet pants.

It's time to dress our puppet. Costuming is not as hard as it looks. Almost all clothing patterns for a hand puppet are created using the front and back Body Patterns as a starting point. Patterns for a simple shirt and pants are included in this book. Also included are all the patterns for making Puck's costume. Remember, the patterns are based on the Body Pattern and will have to be cut on the fold of the material for each piece.

The first thing a hand puppet needs is pants. The pants pattern can be used in two ways. First is as an actual pair of pants the puppet might wear. This works best if the leg pattern isn't used. The second way, is as a basic color behind the legs. Usually black is best for this. But, for our purposes, we will use the same material as the legs/tights will be made from. Trace the front & back pants pattern onto the folded over fabric - ensuring the patterns is aligned to the fold. (See Fig # 44) Cut out and, using a 1/4" seam allowance, sew the two sides of the pants together. Turn the finished pants inside out.

Fig. #44 Pants pattern (top) cut out of folded fabric (bottom).

Note: If using a material which will fray, fold over the top of the pants material and make an 1/8″ hem. This is because in some cases, the pants will show over the top of the shirt pattern. Do not hem the bottom.

Now here's the trick for making a great pant/bottom sleeve. Turn the sewn pants inside-out and insert into the finished body sleeve ensuring the finish surfaces of the pants and sleeve are together. (See Fig # 45) Match the fronts and backs, pin at the bottom, and sew around the bottom of the body sleeve to join the two pieces. (See Fig #46)

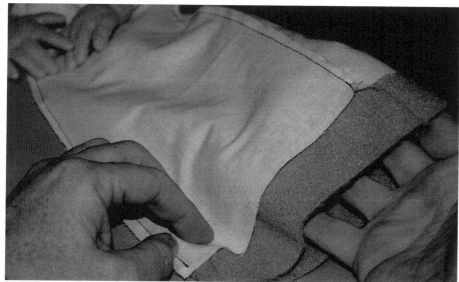

Fig. #45 The pants are inserted into the body sleeve so the finish sides are together.

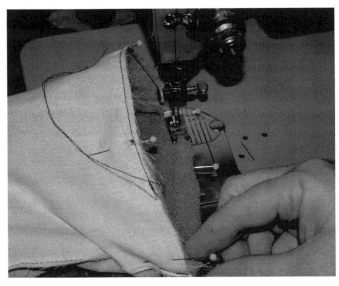

Fig. #46 Pin and machine sew the pants and body sleeve together around the bottom.

Remove the pins and pull the pants out of the sleeve, causing it to become reversed again. The rough selvages of the puppet body and the pants should be on the outside. Pull the pants up and over the body sleeve, once again reversing the pants so the finish side is now on the outside. Smooth out the seam at the bottom of the puppet body and once more machine stitch around the bottom of the puppet. (See Fig #47)

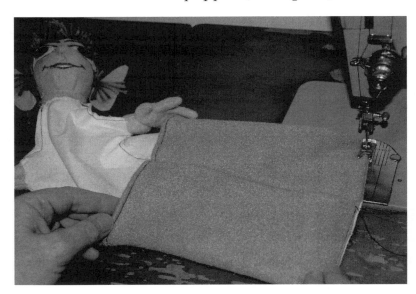

Fig. #47 Pull the pants outside the body sleeve then up over it and sew again around the bottom. Notice the hem sewn at the top of the pants for a finished look.

Step 2 - Making a shirt & tunic.

Using the same construction steps as the body and pants, make the shirt.

Note: Since our Puck design calls for a bare arm and tunic, I am going to turn the shirt pattern into a skin for the finished puppet by using the flesh colored fabric with the shirt pattern. Sometimes a puppet will call for a complete second body sleeve to be made in the flesh fabric and fitted (with the selvages inside) over the muslin body sleeve. (See Fig # 48)

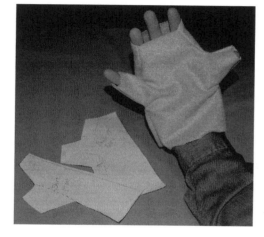

Fig. #48 How a finished shirt should look. However this is going to be Puck's skin.

To place the shirt on the puppet, feed the bottom of the muslin sleeve through the neck of the shirt and pull the shirt up and onto the arms. (See Fig #49) Finish the shirt by hand sewing it onto the neck, both wrists, and at the bottom to the muslin sleeve. If it's to be an actual shirt, it will need cuffs to cover the seams connecting the shirt to the hands. Buttons in front can be added later.

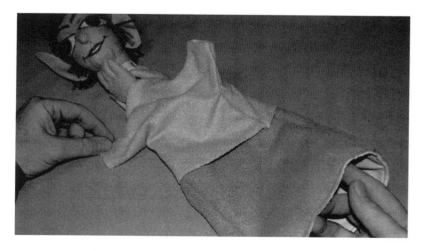

Fig. #49 Insert the puppet body through the shirt neck and pull it down until the arms fit into the shirt sleeves

Pull up the pants and hand sew them onto the finished shirt. (See Fig #50)

Fig. #50 Pin the pants over the shirt and hand sew to the body sleeve.

As mentioned, our Puck needs a tunic rather than a shirt. This is also fairly simple to make. Trace the two (2) tunic patterns onto the fabric as shown. Notice how we have combined the back and two side pieces to create one pattern. This is done by taking the back piece and drawing one side, and then flipping the pattern to get the other drawn side. Now do the same with the front tunic pattern, only flipping them on either side of the finished back pattern. (See Fig #51) Cut out, around the drawn line, to create a single piece.

Fig. #51 Tunic pattern pieces (top) and resulting tunic. **Note**: This tunic isn't lined.

Note: Tunics and such look great in felt or fleece which doesn't fray. If using a cotton material, the tunic will probably have to be lined by doubling the fabric and machine sewing around the drawn line before cutting out the tunic. Cut a slit in the top layer of the tunic back where it won't be seen, and turn inside out. Iron and continue with the steps as outlined. (Same for Sleeve patterns) If the tunic has one color on the outside and another color for the lining, simply place the traced fabric onto a suitable lining fabric, pin, sew, cut out, and turn inside out as described before. See costuming under "Making Marionette" for further instruction.

To finish the tunic, match and machine sew the shoulders together and close the back dart at the top. (See Fig #52) Turn inside out, place on the puppet, pin the tunic in the front. (See Fig #53), and hand sew it closed. Sew the bottom of the tunic to the body sleeve and the pants, as well as to the puppet's neck and arms.

Fig. #52 Sew the back dart closed and the side shoulders together above the arm holes.

Cut out two (2) of Puck's Sleeve pattern from the fabric used for the tunic. Place them aside for use in the next step.

Fig. #53 Tunic top sewn onto the puppet.

Step 3 - Using a hand puppet "false arm."

False arms give the hand puppet some of the elegance a marionette would have, since it allows for a bare arm or full arm which gives the puppet a more human dimension. They are easier to produce and use than most people would imagine. Transfer the False Arm pattern twice onto a doubled piece of the skin fabric. Sew around the drawn line, leaving the wrist open. Cut out the two pieces, turn inside out and stuff. (See Fig #54)

Fig. #54 Fake arm pattern (top), drawn on fabric (right), and cut out and stuffed (bottom). **Note:** Tunic sleeves (left) ready for sewing.

Note: If making a shirt for the puppet instead of a tunic, make the shirt from the desired material just like we did for the flesh/shirt on Puck. Then use the same shirt fabric for the fake arms, attached them to the puppet as described below, and finish with a fake cuff to hide the joint of the wrist and arm.

Secure the stuffed arms onto the puppet body (See Fig #55) by sewing each arm onto the puppet's wrist. Be careful not to sew the inside glove closed which would prevent the puppeteer's finger slipping into the puppet's hand. Keeping a hand inside the puppet while sewing pieces to the body is the easiest way. Attach the top of the body sleeve's shoulder, and lightly sew to the body near the elbow. Three sewn points altogether.

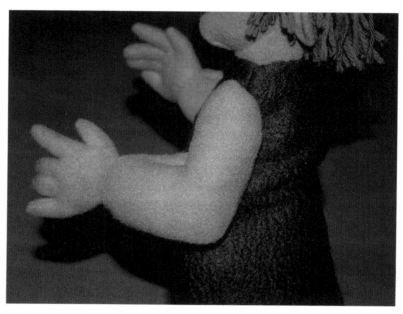

Fig. #55 The fake arm is sewn to the puppet at the wrist, the top of the arm, and at the base of the elbow. Hide the stitches as much as possible. **Note**: Do not attach the arms until the sleeves have been completed and fitted to the arms.

For the Puck figure, the sleeve "caps" are attached to the fake arms before the arms are attached to the puppet. Sew the darts closed on each of the previously cut out sleeves, then stitch closed from point A to point B. The two sleeve "caps" are placed over the tops of the fake arms and lightly attached with hidden stitches. Then the arms are stitched onto the hand puppet body. (See Fig #55 & 56) The sleeve dart should be on the back of the arm, while the A to B stitching is on the inside facing front.

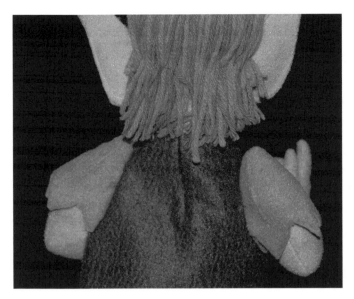

Fig. #56 Puck's false arms with sleeves attached. **Note**: The sleeve dart at the back of the sleeve.

Step 4 - Making hand puppet legs and shoes.

Like the arms, trace the leg pattern onto the folded chosen fabric and machine sew. Although the fake leg with shoe pattern is nice, and makes a cute puppet, I like my figures to have a more dimensional finished shoe. So I've included in Puck patterns a new leg design which doesn't have the shoe included. This pattern will create a leg which can be fitted into a larger type of shoe. (See Fig #57)

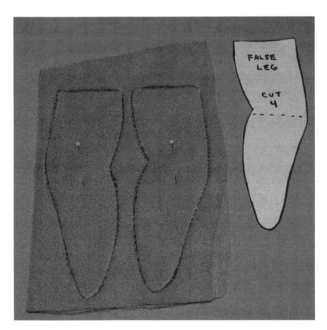

Fig. #57 Puck's leg pattern (right) is traced onto fabric (left).

Cut out the legs and turn inside out. The legs need a little weight to make them swing and hang over the stage. Sand is a convenient solution. Keep a covered can filled with clean white sand with the supplies. Using a funnel to prevent spills, fill the bottom of the leg with 2" of sand, then stuff with kapok to the middle of the leg. Machine sew across the back of the leg (back seam up) creating a bend for the leg. Finish off by stuffing the rest of the leg and sewing it closed at the top. (See Fig #58)

Our leg for Puck is one color and cut out of the clothing material. This is because he is supposed to be wearing tights. But most often a hand puppet will be wearing pants instead of hose. For this we have included in the costuming patterns a pants leg. Simple to use. Trace and cut out two (2) pants legs from the selected pants material. Hem at the bottom, and then machine sew the back side Points A to B. Turn inside out. (See Fig #59)

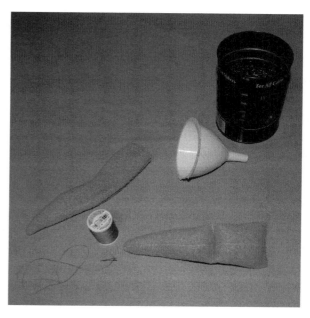

Fig. #58 Finished leg (bottom) is shown with un-stuffed leg ((left).

Slip the stuffed leg into the pants leg as shown. (See Fig #59) Attach legs as shown in Fig #65, and sew the top of the pants leg fabric to the puppet body.

> **Note:** Turn under the fabric at the top to give a finished look at the waist.

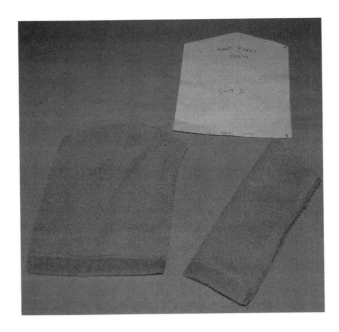

Fig. #59 Pant leg pattern (upper), cut from fabric (left) and sewn at side seam. **Note**: The bottom hem.

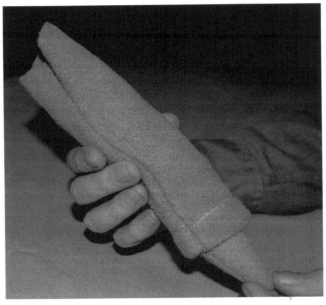

Fig. #60 Inserting a stuffed leg into the finished pants leg.

Let's discuss shoes. For my puppets, I like to use the shoe pattern included with the marionette patterns. (See Chapter 4.) Trace and cut two (2) of each piece out of the shoe fabric. Also, cut two (2) cardboard pieces of the bottom sole shoe pattern. Remember to make the cardboard inserts slightly smaller so they will fit into the finished sewn shoe. (See Fig #61)

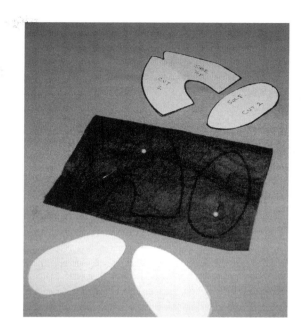

Fig. #61 Shoe pattern (top) traced onto fabric (center). **Note**: Two cardboard sole inserts (bottom) are also cut out

Starting at the tip of the shoe top piece, sew it to the sole from front to center back. . (See Fig #62) Flip over and do the other side. The bottom sole section should now be completely enclosed.

Turn the sewn shoe inside out and place a cardboard piece into the foot. (See Fig #63) Remember the cardboard piece has to be smaller than the original in order to fit nicely into the shoe. Put a little stuffing into the toe of the shoe and then add a tiny bit of sand for more weight. Now fill with stuffing.

Fig. #62 Sewing the sole to the shoe top from front to back.

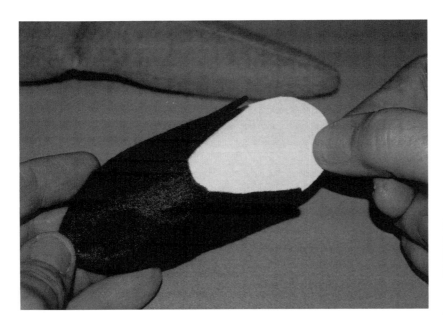

Fig. #63 Placing the cardboard sole inside the shoe before filling with kapok, sand, and more kapok.

Place the stuffed leg into the back of the sewn shoe and pin. The leg should be the final stuffing needed to fill out the foot. Close the sides of the shoe pattern around the leg and hand sew shoe's back seam closed. Now sew the shoe to the ankle of the leg. (See Fig #64)

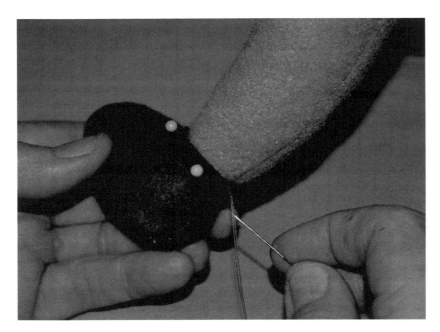

Fig. #64 The leg is inserted into the shoe and the shoe's back seam is stitched closed before the shoe is sewn to the ankle.

With the shoes attached, the legs are ready to place onto the puppet body. Pin the legs onto the front of the hand puppet glove and sew at the place where the pants and shirt have intersected. (See Fig #65) Hand sew at the top of each leg to secure to the puppet. Check balance and position while sewing.

> **Note:** If the puppet has pants legs, now is the time to stitch them over the top of the legs and onto the hand puppet body glove. (After first sewing legs to body.)

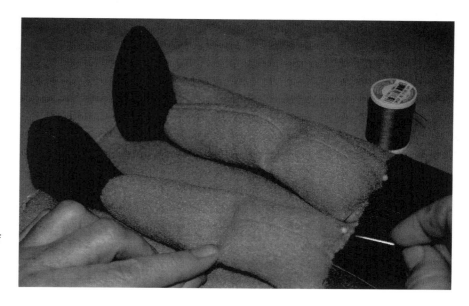

Fig. #65 Legs are aligned onto the front of the hand puppet body. **Note**: Leg seams running up the front of the tights.

On the use of arms & Legs, Lewis Mahlmann suggests:

> *"Use both the false arms and false legs sparingly. I suggest you don't use false arms on animals or cute things. It takes away from the sweet puppet-like quality and their charm. Do be free to use them where costumes need the beauty of the arms, legs & sleeves."*

Step 5 - Adding "glitz" and other costume extras.

The Puck puppet is almost finished. We have to add all the things that complete the look of the finished figure. These include: the collar with bells, flowered belt, bottom section of tunic, and the fancy elf boots. (See Fig #66)

Fig. #66 Belt trim (top) bottom of the tunic (center), boot pieces (middle right), collar (lower right) and Pan Pipes (lower left).

Puck's Collar: Trace the Collar pattern onto a piece of doubled fabric (as we have done with many of the puppet parts). It should look like the one in Fig #66. Machine sew around the drawn lines and cut out. Cut a slit in the backside of the sewn collar, turn inside out, and hand sew the slit shut. This now becomes the back of the collar. Sew bells to each of the peaked tips of the collar. Gather with a running stitch the top of the ruff and pull tightly around the puppet's neck and sew the collar to the neck of the puppet. Done.

Puck's Belt: The measurements for our belt are 13-1/2" x 3/4". Trace on folded fabric and machine sew, leaving one end open. Turn inside out and iron. Hot glue flowers to the belt and sew on the puppet after the tunic bottom has been added. Done.

Bottom of Puck's Tunic: The pattern for this piece is found with the marionette Puck's costume patterns at the end of Chapter 5. Following the steps used to make Puck's collar, make the tunic bottom. Remember to draw two sides of the pattern at the fold. It should look like the finished one in Fig #66. When turned and finished, line it up on the puppet's body so the flowered petal ends fall just below where the legs are sewn to the body. Pin and sew around the outside of the puppet's waist. Now place the finished flowered belt over the top of the bottom piece. This gives the look of the tunic being one piece instead of two. Sew the belt around Puck's waist at the top and the bottom. Done.

Finishing Puck's Boots: Draw the Boot Top and Boot Toe patterns onto a piece of doubled shoe fabric. Sew around the drawn line. Remember: Leave the boot toe open at the areas where there are no drawn dotted lines. Cut out the boot tops, make a slit in the back of the fabric and turn them inside out. Sew the slit closed, iron, and attach the bottom of the boot top to the ankle where the shoe has been sewn on. Close at the front of the bottom and sew to the shoe. Cut out the boot toe pieces, turn inside out, and stuff the toe solidly with kapok. Pin to the front of the finished shoe and hand sew around the toe section. (See Fig #67) We have glitzed the boots with a threaded sequin band wrapped around the seam where the boot top meets the shoe. This gives a nice look. Hot glue or sew the trim to the boot. Done.

> **Note:** Sometimes to give an interesting look, we will make the sole and shoe top two different colors. Making the bottom sole darker adds a unique look for the finished shoe. Try it sometime.

Puck's Pan Pipes: Odd props are fun to make or find. For Puck's pipes, we used wooden beads from an old beaded curtain for the basic structure. Hot gluing the round sections together and gluing/ nailing beads to the top of them for the mouth piece. To finish it off, we wrapped a light brown trim around the wood pieces and glued. Done. The pipe is then glued or sewn onto the hand.

The puppet is now finished and looking great! (See Fig #67) So many different types of characters can be made just the way we made this particular hand puppet.

Fig. #67 The finished Puck hand puppet. (Color photo on back cover.)

Experiment and keep thinking up different ways to use the hand puppet patterns. We've given the basics and now it's up to you to find new ways to expand upon our tutorial. I would like to give a few more costuming notes before we leave the world of hand puppets.

What if the puppet is wearing a skirt or apron? Very common clothing articles and easy to make. Here are the measurements for making a proper woman's attire:

A full gathered top skirt: This formula is the length of the skirt by two times the waist measurement. For Puck it would be 11" x 26". Cut out one piece of fabric, sew closed the side, hem the bottom, and make a gathering stitch around the top of the skirt. Pull the thread and gather the fabric to the waist of the puppet. Sew the skirt to the puppet body and cover with a belt. Done.

A less full petticoat or under skirt: The formula for this one is: the length of the skirt by one-and-a-half times the waist measurement. Or, for Puck - 11" x 19-1/2." Follow the above directions for a full skirt. Done.

An Apron: Very easy. The formula is the length of an apron by one-and-a-half times half of the waist measurement. Gather at the top and sew to an apron band which is four times the waist measurement. Add lace around apron body for design purposes. Done.

A gathered sleeve at the bottom: Puffed sleeves are easy. The top of the sleeve remains the same size to fit into the shirt, while the bottom of the sleeve is two times the wrist measurement. Gather at the bottom, sew to hand, and cover with trim or cuff. Done.

If you are having any trouble with these, don't forget to look at books on costuming for the theater. Puppets are costumed just the way you would build a wardrobe for an actor.

Let's move on to marionettes.

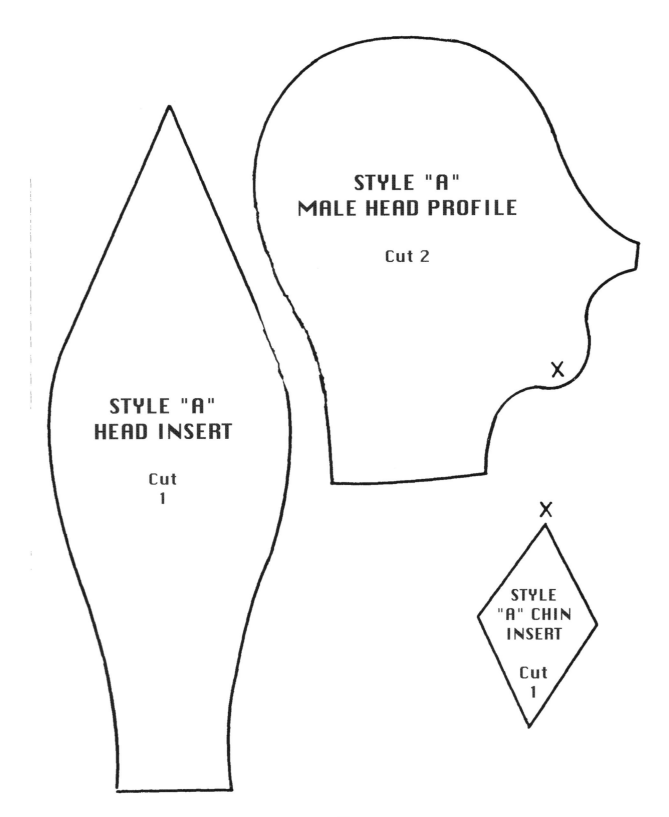

STYLE "A"
MALE HEAD PROFILE

Cut 2

STYLE "A"
HEAD INSERT

Cut
1

X

X

STYLE
"A" CHIN
INSERT

Cut
1

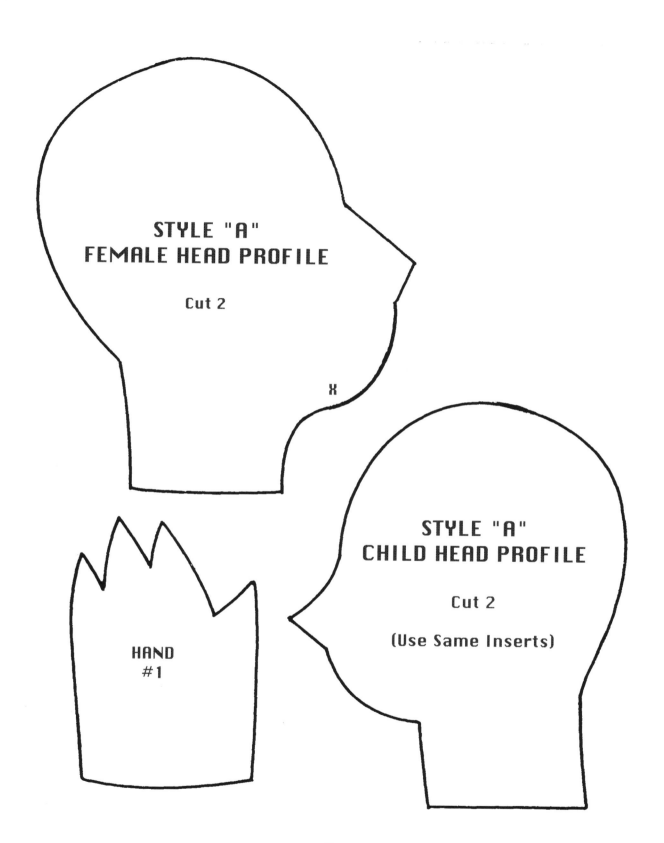

STYLE "A"
FEMALE HEAD PROFILE

Cut 2

X

HAND
#1

STYLE "A"
CHILD HEAD PROFILE

Cut 2

(Use Same Inserts)

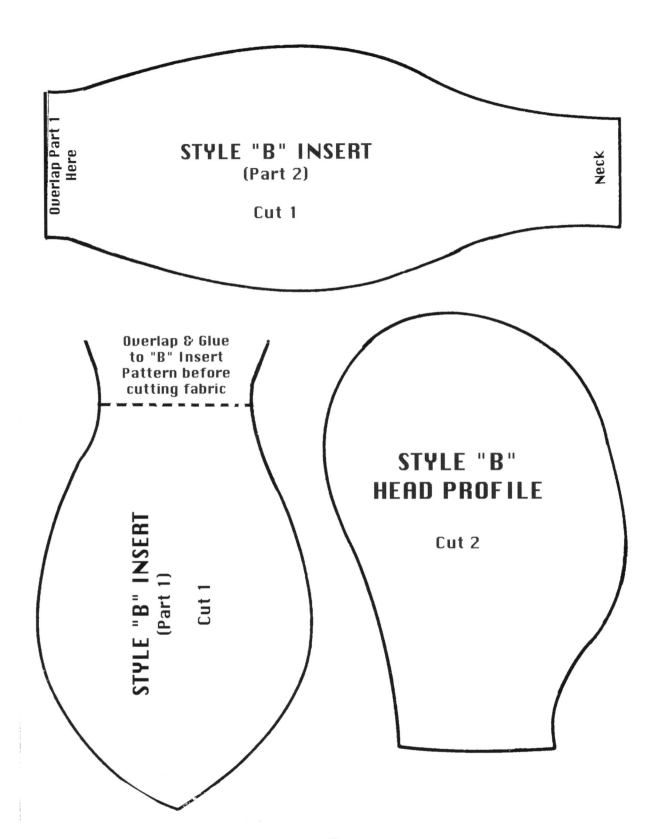

STYLE "B" INSERT
(Part 2)

Cut 1

Overlap Part 1
Here

Neck

Overlap & Glue
to "B" Insert
Pattern before
cutting fabric

STYLE "B" INSERT
(Part 1)

Cut 1

STYLE "B"
HEAD PROFILE

Cut 2

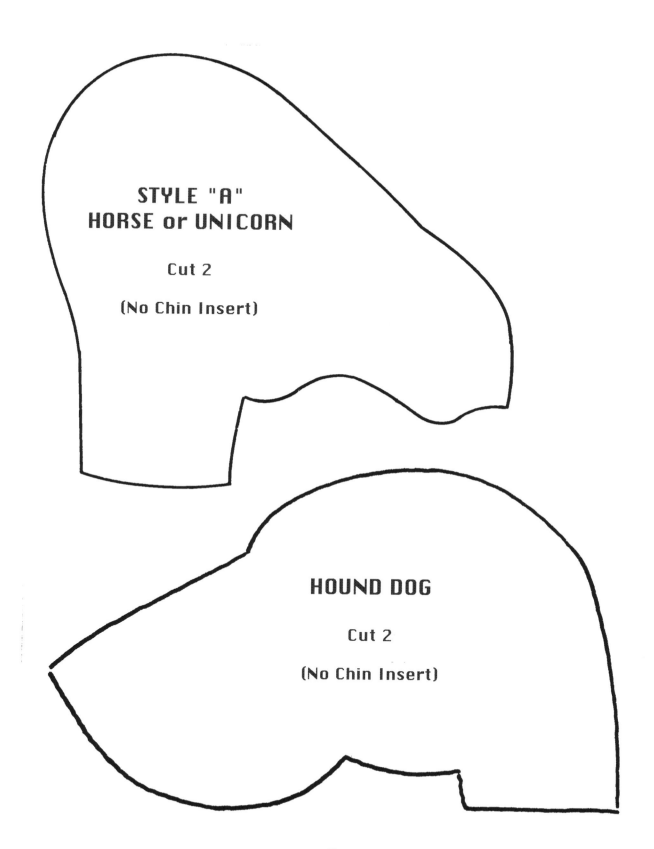

STYLE "A"
HORSE or UNICORN

Cut 2

(No Chin Insert)

HOUND DOG

Cut 2

(No Chin Insert)

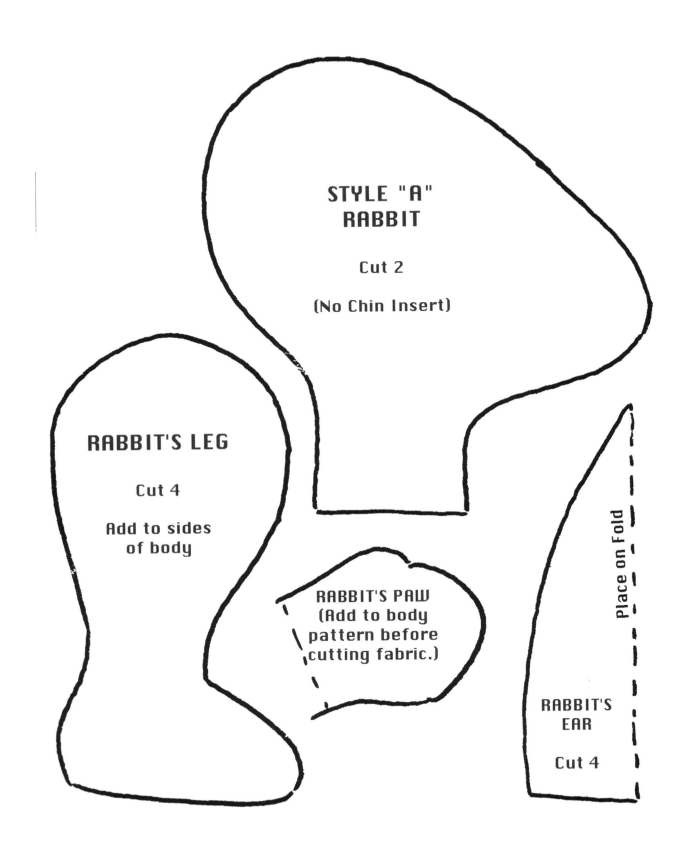

STYLE "A"
RABBIT

Cut 2

(No Chin Insert)

RABBIT'S LEG

Cut 4

Add to sides
of body

RABBIT'S PAW
(Add to body
pattern before
cutting fabric.)

Place on Fold

RABBIT'S
EAR

Cut 4

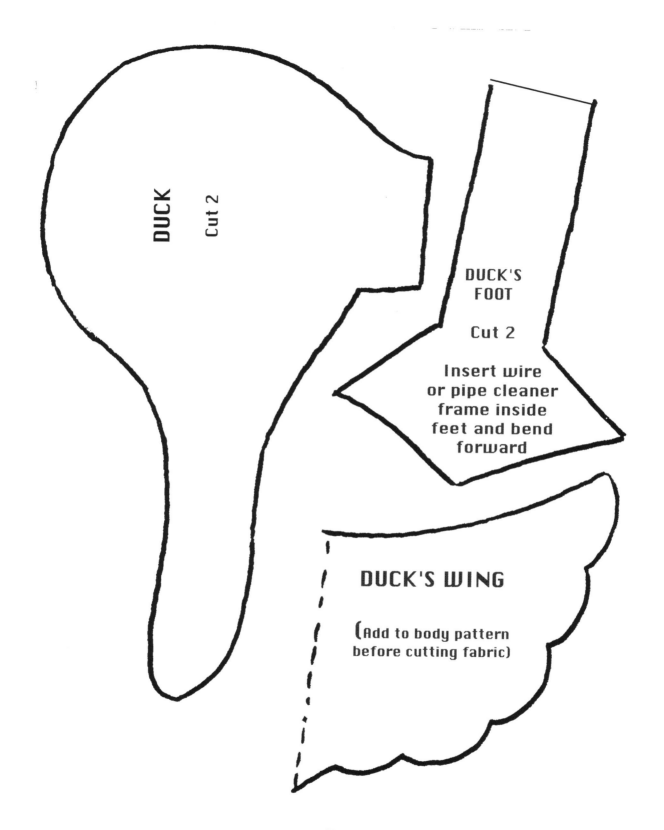

DUCK

Cut 2

DUCK'S
FOOT

Cut 2

Insert wire
or pipe cleaner
frame inside
feet and bend
forward

DUCK'S WING

(Add to body pattern
before cutting fabric)

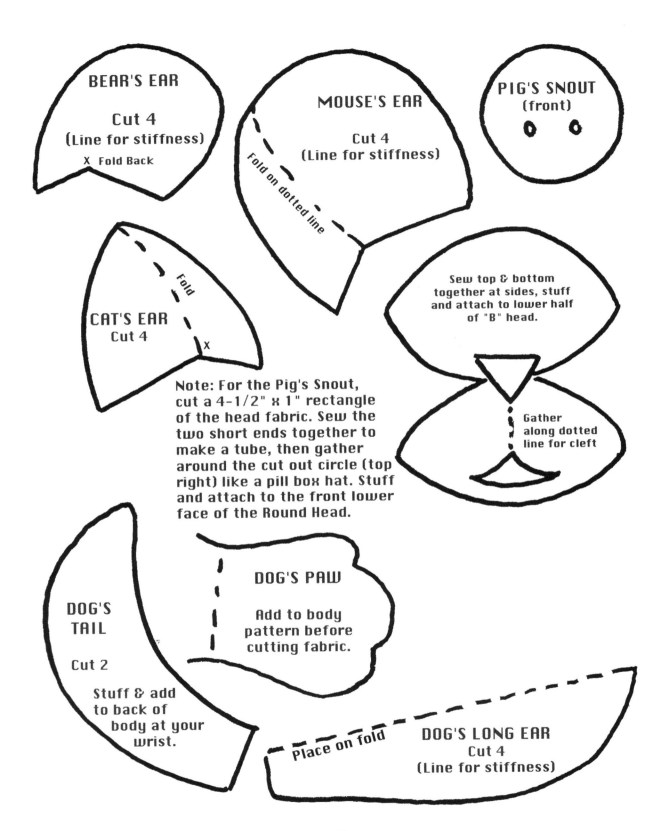

BEAR'S EAR

Cut 4
(Line for stiffness)

X Fold Back

MOUSE'S EAR

Cut 4
(Line for stiffness)

Fold on dotted line

PIG'S SNOUT
(front)

Fold

CAT'S EAR
Cut 4

X

Sew top & bottom
together at sides, stuff
and attach to lower half
of "B" head.

Gather
along dotted
line for cleft

Note: For the Pig's Snout,
cut a 4-1/2" x 1" rectangle
of the head fabric. Sew the
two short ends together to
make a tube, then gather
around the cut out circle (top
right) like a pill box hat. Stuff
and attach to the front lower
face of the Round Head.

DOG'S PAW

Add to body
pattern before
cutting fabric.

DOG'S TAIL

Cut 2

Stuff & add
to back of
body at your
wrist.

Place on fold

DOG'S LONG EAR
Cut 4
(Line for stiffness)

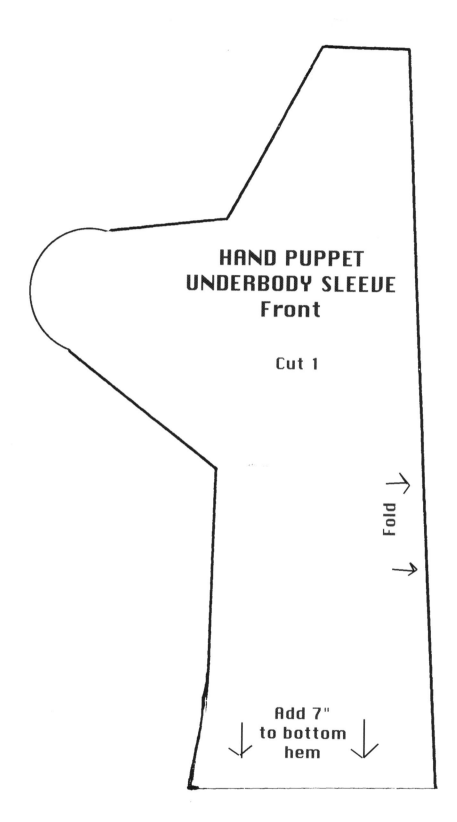

**HAND PUPPET
UNDERBODY SLEEVE
Front**

Cut 1

Fold →

→

Add 7"
to bottom
hem
↓   ↓

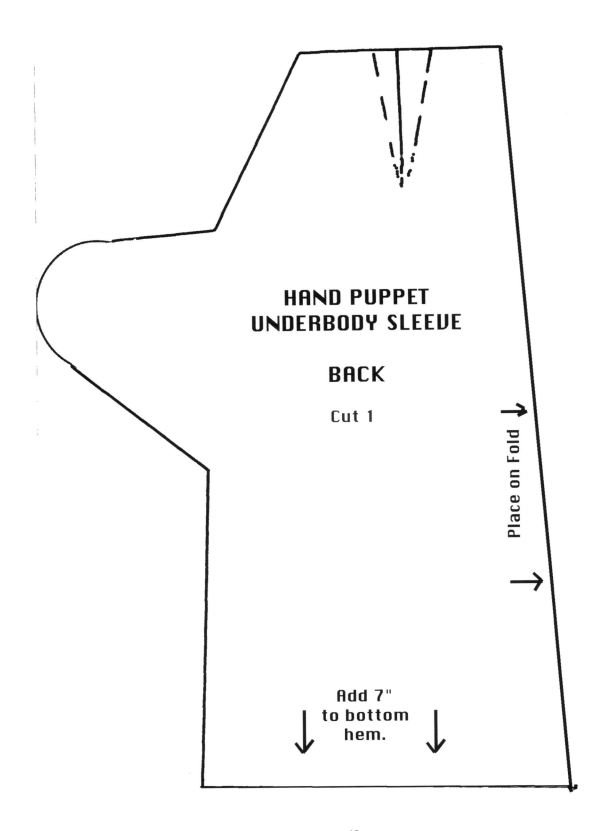

**HAND PUPPET
UNDERBODY SLEEVE**

BACK

Cut 1

Place on Fold

Add 7"
to bottom
hem.

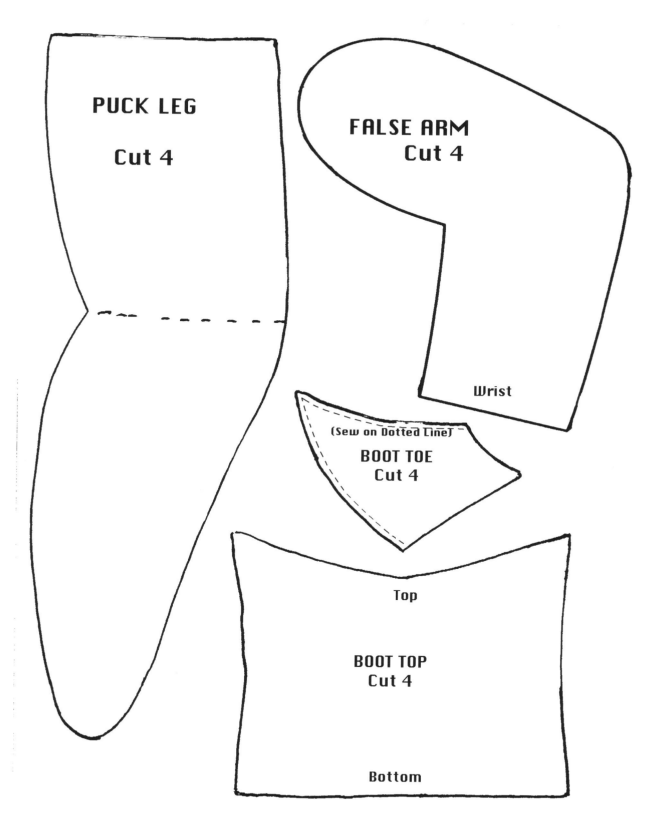

PUCK LEG

Cut 4

FALSE ARM

Cut 4

Wrist

(Sew on Dotted Line)

BOOT TOE
Cut 4

Top

BOOT TOP
Cut 4

Bottom

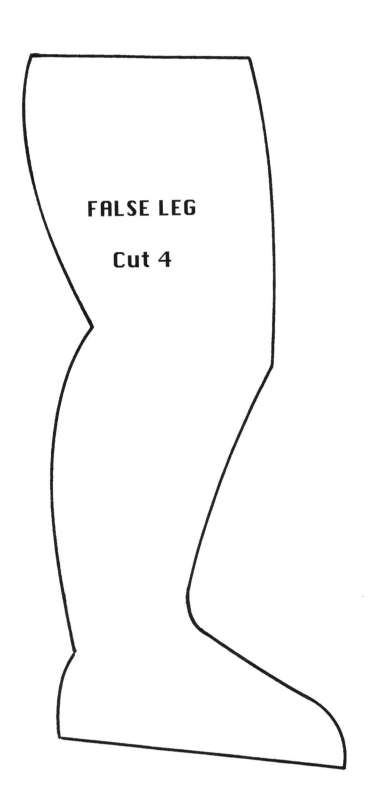

FALSE LEG

Cut 4

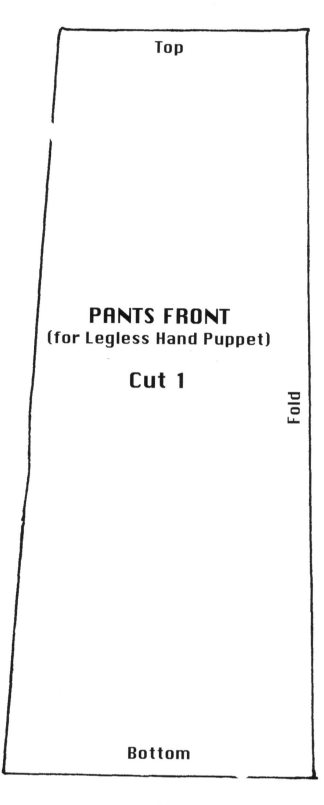

Top

PANTS FRONT
(for Legless Hand Puppet)

Cut 1

Fold

Bottom

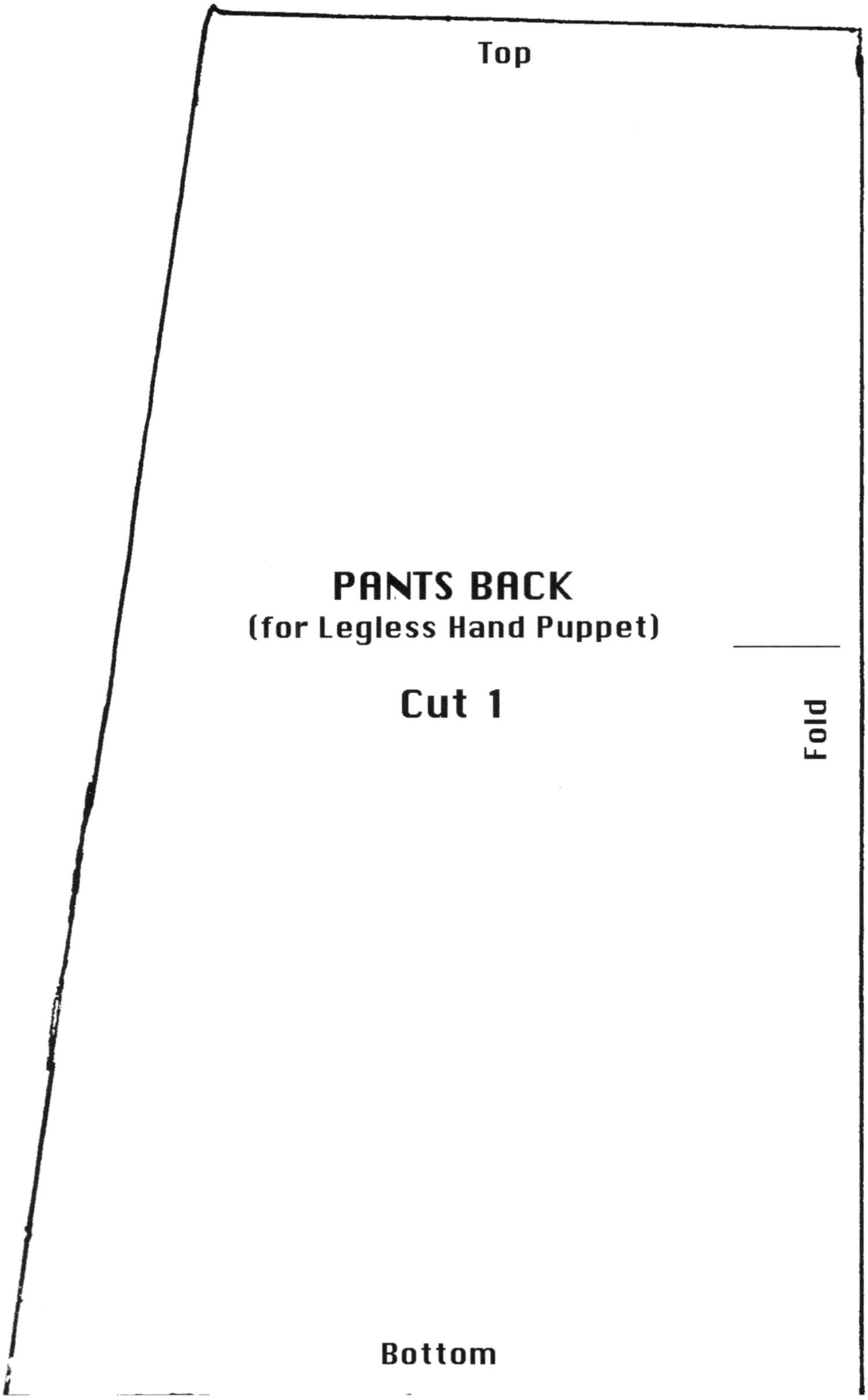

Top

PANTS BACK
(for Legless Hand Puppet)

Cut 1

Fold

Bottom

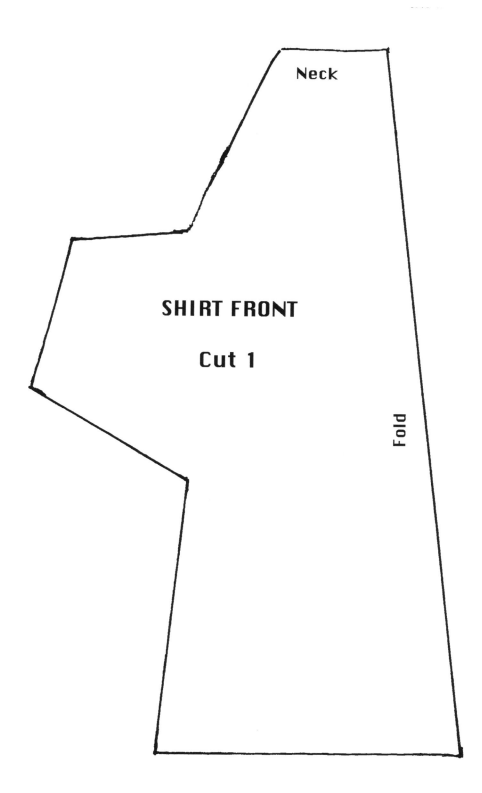

Neck

SHIRT FRONT

Cut 1

Fold

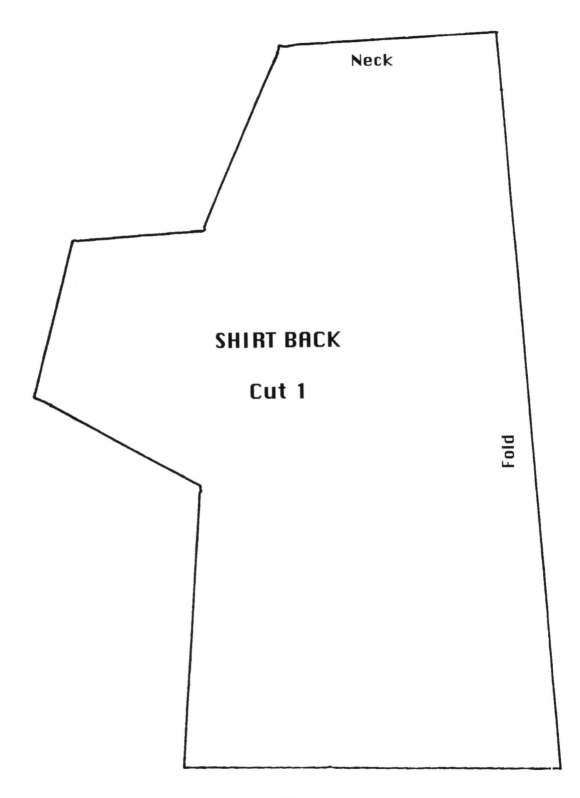

Neck

SHIRT BACK

Cut 1

Fold

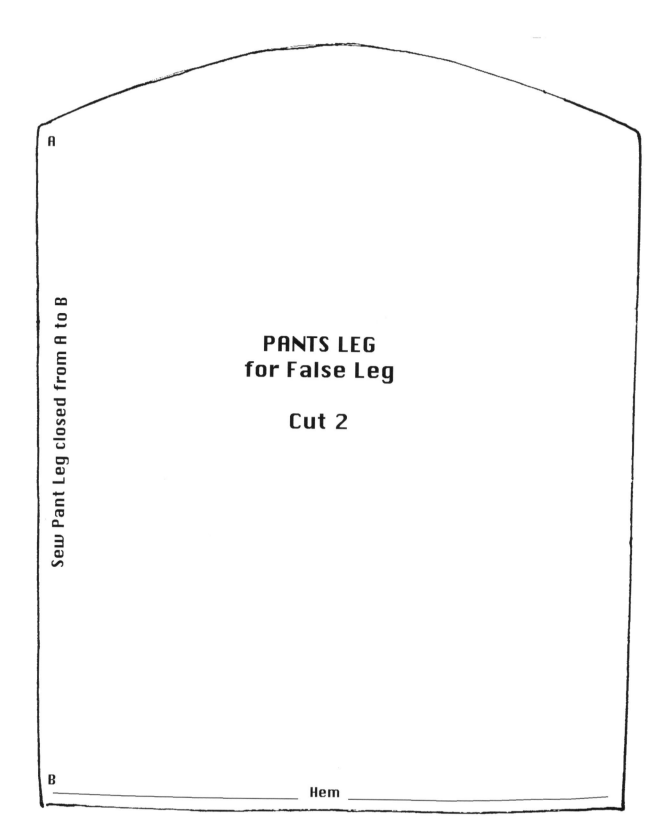

A

Sew Pant Leg closed from A to B

PANTS LEG
for False Leg

Cut 2

B

Hem

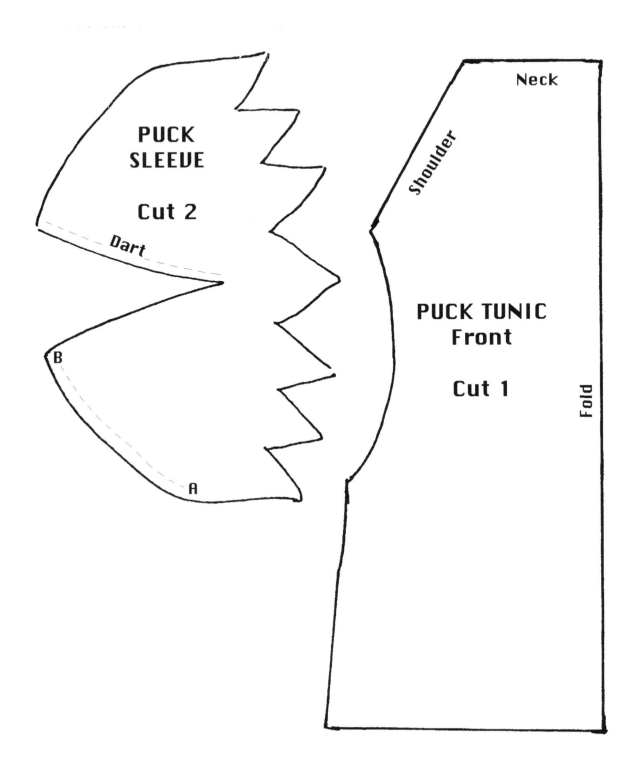

PUCK
SLEEVE

Cut 2

Dart

B

A

Neck

Shoulder

PUCK TUNIC
Front

Cut 1

Fold

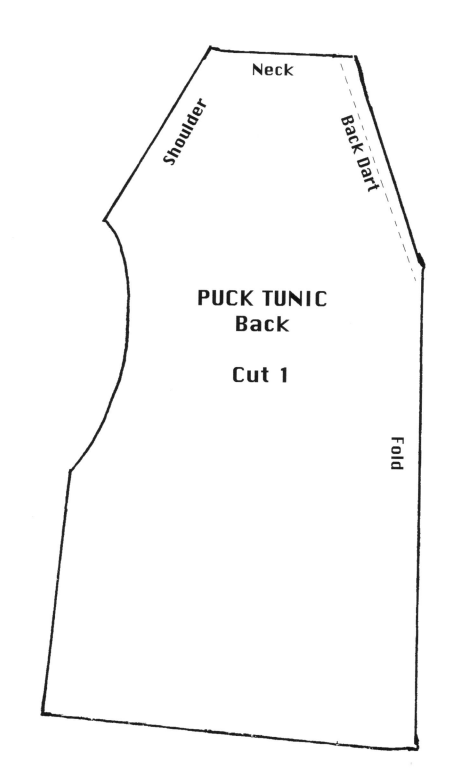

Neck

Shoulder

Back Dart

PUCK TUNIC
Back

Cut 1

Fold

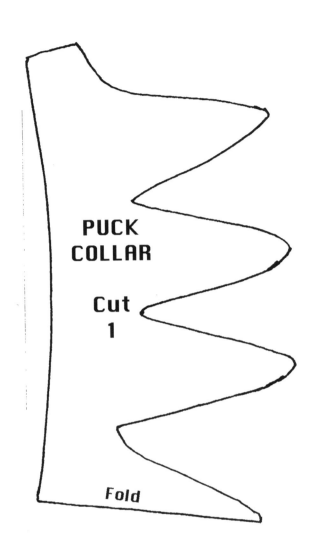

PUCK
COLLAR

Cut
1

Fold

Chapter 3: MAKING A MORE COMPLICATED HEAD

The next pattern is my favorite because it gives the face, and shape of the head, a great elongated look. I suggest using this pattern for marionettes and rod puppets. I particularly like this pattern because it creates a larger head with a neck which can be changed to any length. Since we are making a marionette next, I will reproduce Puck's head using this pattern and the same steps as used for the other hand puppet heads. Always remember to choose the right head pattern for the look of the puppet. Although we used the 'A' head for the hand puppet, my design was always meant to use this angular head pattern. Notice the change in look when the marionette is finally completed.

STYLE 'C' ANGULAR HEAD

Step 1 - Assembling and sewing the puppet patterns.

Begin, as always, by copying or tracing the patterns from the book and cutting out the copied pieces. Trace these patterns onto the desired head material and cut out the pieces. For this head there will be two (2) side pieces, one (1) face front, one (1) crown of the head and one (1) neck piece. (See Fig #1)

Fig #1: Head patterns (upper left) traced onto the face material (lower), and also cut out of muslin (upper right) for the demonstration head. **Note:** The face material is folded over for cutting the two side pieces.

Fig. #2: Face (left) and crown (right) with properly sewn darts.

Machine sew closed the three darts located on the face front and crown pattern. (See Fig #2)

Using an approximately 1/8" seam allowance, pin one side of the head profile to the face front. Start sewing at the top of the dart in the forehead and stop at the chin. (See Fig #3)

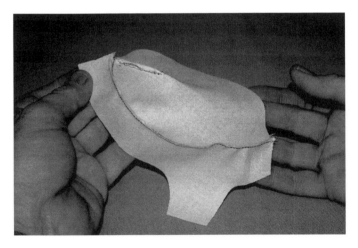

Fig. #3 Sew each profile to the face.

Pin and sew the opposite side of the head profile to the other side of the face front, then sew the two profile pieces together at the top and bottom of the face section. (See Fig #4)

Sew the crown section to the back of the head.

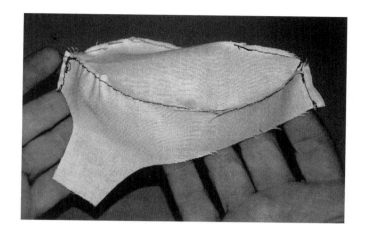

Fig. #4: After sewing both profile pieces to the face, sew them closed at the top and bottom.

Note: With the D dart at the top of the head, and the C dart at the bottom, pin the crown onto the back of the face sides and sew all the way around. (See Fig #5) There will probably be some excess from the side pieces left over. Don't worry, we'll deal with that soon.

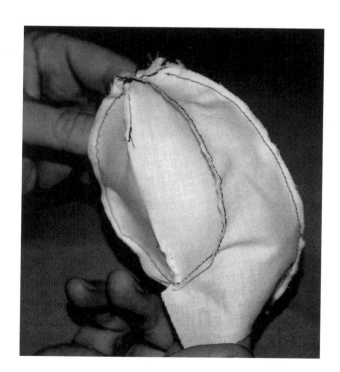

Fig. #5: Crown section shown properly stitched onto the puppet head.

Here comes a tricky part. Insert the neck piece into the hollow head and starting at the middle of the neck piece, pin it to the chin front. (See Fig #6) Then pin along the sides of the profile pieces and sew around the edge. Pull the neck out of the inner head.

Sew the back of the neck closed, starting at the bottom of the neck section and ending at the bottom of the crown dart. (See Fig #7) Sew a straight line. There will be a little overhang from the side pieces.

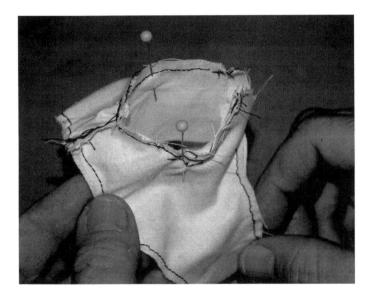

Fig. #6: Sew the neck to the head by placing it into the hollow head. Pin and sew around the neck of the two profile sections. Pull the neck out.

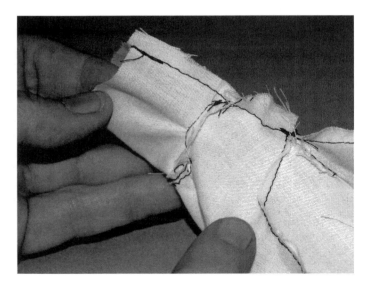

Fig. #7: Sew closed from the bottom of the neck piece to the bottom of the crown dart.

Turn the head inside out and check for any weak seams. Repair as needed. Stuff the head, being especially careful to fill out the cheek and chin areas, and insert the cardboard neck tube. (See Chapter 2) Use a paint brush handle to stuff into tight areas and to add stuffing around the tube.

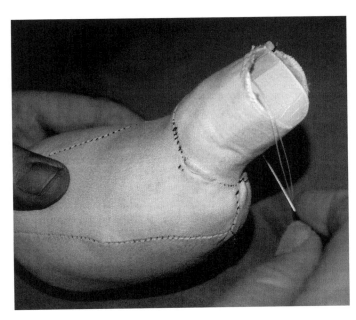

Fig. #8: Trim down the neck and sew the cardboard tube in place.

Note: I like to cut 1-1/4" off the bottom of the neck at this time. Remember, the neck is longer than needed, and should be trimmed to suit the puppet. Sew the neck to the tube as done in previous heads. (See Fig #8)

Step 2 - Giving the head more definition by using the method of "dimpling."

"Dimpling", or needle sculpting, is the process of using a strong thread to alter the head shape by pulling the thread and the material tightly in one direction. Many fabric doll faces in the early 70's were created this way. I have chosen to use a polyester fiber for stuffing this muslin head since it will pull things tighter and show the indentations better. Normally I use kapok, which packs tighter and does not show as many puckers around the seams.

There are many ways to dimple a stuffed head. Here are four popular methods which can enhance the design of the finished puppet.

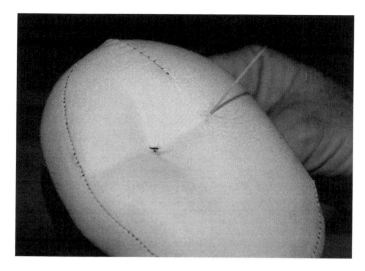

Fig. #9: Pulling in the eye sockets to create indentions will bring out the forehead and cheeks. Notice the long needle.

Eye sockets: This is the most common one. By indenting the eyes, the forehead is enlarged slightly above the eyes and at the same time the cheeks become more rounded. Lightly mark in pencil where the eyes will be. Thread a very long needle with strong carpet thread and poke the needle from the center of an eye socket to the back of the head. Reverse back through the head and then again to the back. Pull and tie off the thread. Repeat with other eye socket. (See Fig #9)

> **Note:** It is always a good and safe practice to tie off the stitches with three knots to ensure the threads will not unravel.

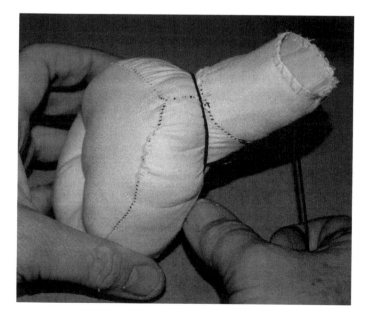

Fig. #10: Plumping up the cheek and chin area while defining the neck and jowel line.

Rounding out the chin and cheeks: With needle and thread, catch one side of the face behind the cheek, and below the ear line, catch the thread under the chin, then on the same point as the anchor stitch on opposite side of the head. Pull the thread to tighten the line. Reverse the thread back under the chin, pull to fill out the bottom of the face and help define the neck from the jowl. Tie off at the starting point. (See Fig #10)

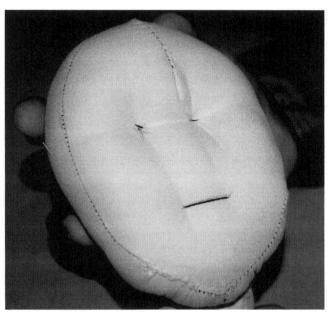

Fig. #11: Smile dimples sewn into place.

Adding dimples and smile: Another fun technique is to add some dimples to the mouth line. Lightly pencil where the mouth is going to be on the face. Starting at the back of the head, bring the thread through and out one side of the smile line. Follow the pencil line across the mouth and push the thread through from the opposite corner of the mouth to the back of the head. Pull the thread tightly until mouth puckers and dimples form. Tie off the thread at the back of the head. (See Fig #11)

Indenting the face to give a figure '8' shape: Here's another fun thing to try. On one side of the face at the ear line, use a long needle to pull the thread through to the opposite ear line and out. Pull tightly, wrap the thread around the back of the head and tie off at the first ear line. This method will pull in the middle sides of the face and create a figure '8' shape to the face front. Experiment and see what happens.

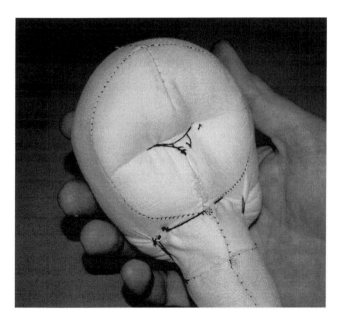

Fig. #12: How the back of the head might look when the "dimpling" is finished.

All of the threads, when tied off, should be hidden at the back or lower sides of the finished head. (See Fig #12) They will be covered by hair and/or hats when finished.

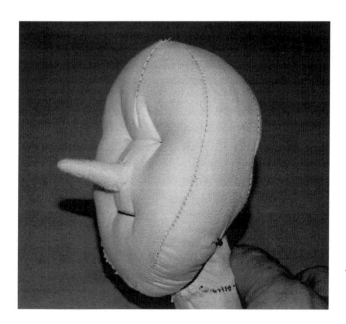

Fig. #13: Muslin head is "dimpled" and the patterned nose is added.

Shaping the face and creating new ways to sculpt with this "dimpling" method is lots of fun. There are no wrong ways to do this. If you don't like what you've done, simply cut the thread and massage out the indentations to the puppet head.

Fig. #14: The finished marionette Puck head and a muslin head.

To make the pointed nose, fold the cut out nose (Page 88) along the dotted line and stitch along the long open side. Turn inside out, stuff, then hand stitch the small triangular tab to seal in the stuffing. Then sew the nose to the puppet's face.

Fig #14 shows our finished Marionette Puck head. We've used a more solid stuffing material and have also applied the first three methods of "dimpling" explained above. When the head is covered with hair, the ears, eyes and nose are added, and the makeup is applied, any blemishes are quickly forgiven! Notice I've made a round nose like the one we fabricated for our style 'B' head. (Chapter 2)

It's time to start making a marionette body for our Elfin head.

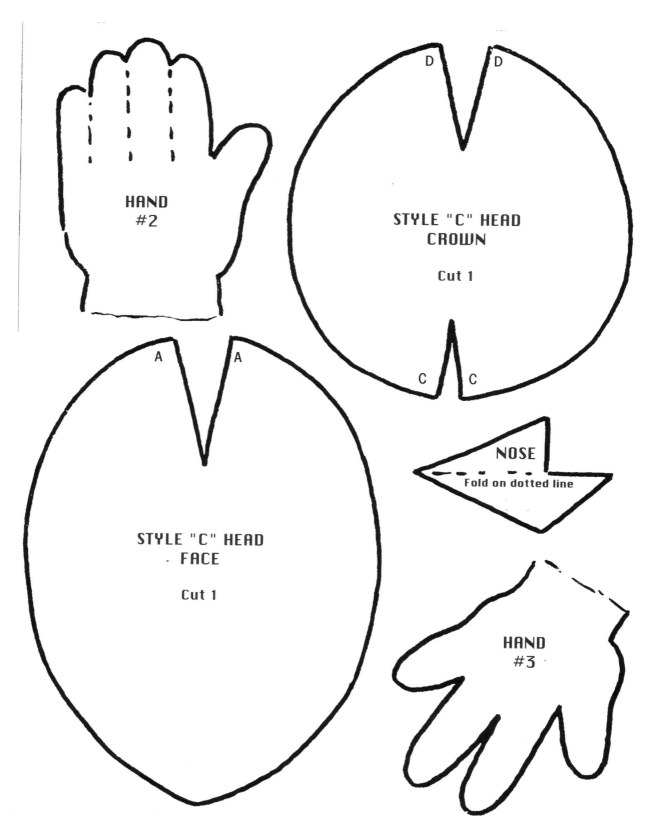

HAND
#2

STYLE "C" HEAD
CROWN

Cut 1

D   D

C   C

A   A

STYLE "C" HEAD
- FACE

Cut 1

NOSE
Fold on dotted line

HAND
#3

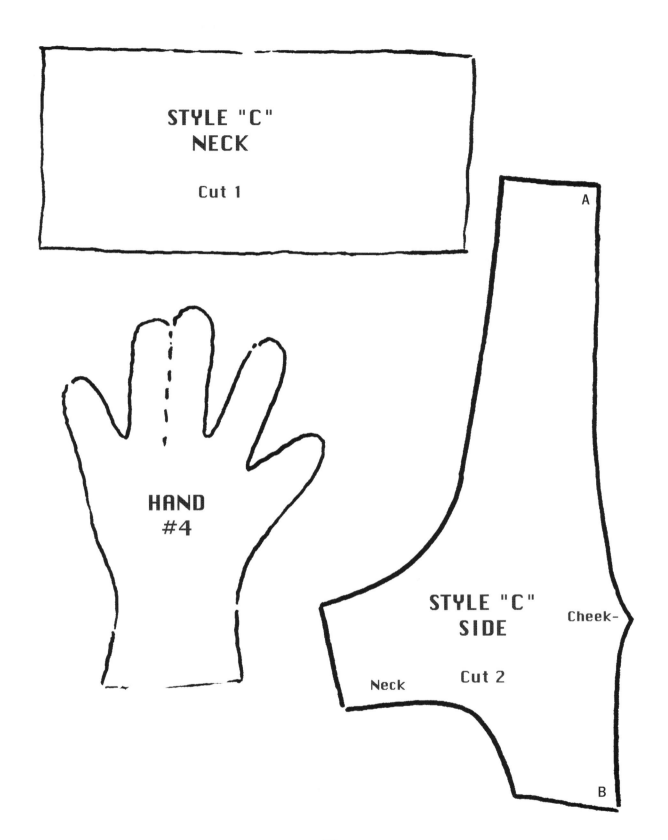

STYLE "C"
NECK

Cut 1

HAND
#4

STYLE "C"
SIDE

Cut 2

Neck

Cheek-

A

B

CHAPTER 4: THE FAIRYLAND MARIONETTE

While hand puppets may be our puppet of choice at the Storybook Theater, marionettes are saved for special productions. If our show calls for spectacular costumes, romantic settings, or a "classical fairy tale look", it is often performed with marionettes. Although its movements are not as intimate as the hand puppet, the sight of a full figure on strings, moving across a scenic landscape, speaks volumes. And don't worry, an audience is always very forgiving of seeing the strings along with the puppet.

Having decided to make a marionette, follow the basics of design as discussed in the second chapter. The Puck marionette we will make is simple, sewn & stuffed, and uses very little wood in the construction. No carving or casting, just sewing and stringing! As before, we have included a list of materials needed for the marionette:

1) Felt or fleece colors for hands and head
2) Unbleached muslin for creating the body parts
3) Chosen materials and trims for the costume
4) Threads: sewing and optional embroidery floss for the above materials
5) The choice of stuffing for body parts
6) Yarns or furs for wigs
7) Faceted buttons for eyes
8) Small makeup selection of eye shadows for facial details
9) Bendable, thin cardboard for the joints and wig templates
10) Pipe cleaners for the fingers of hands
11) Wood dowels for neck and body pieces
12) For the control:
      24" length of wood measuring 3/4" x 1/2"
      1/4" dowel
      Strong cord

13) Screw eyes, staples, spray paint as needed
14) Black nylon string for marionette movement
15) Marionette Costumer (see design) - optional
14) Sand for filling legs & shoes
And of course....scissors, pins, needles, masking tape, marking
   pens, and paper for extra patterns

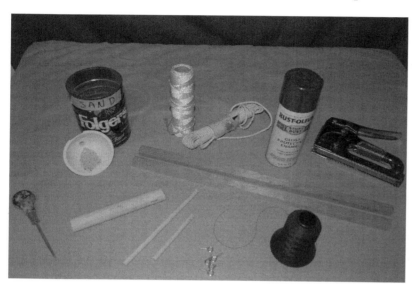

Fig. #1: Some of the suggested new materials ready for construction

Remember: having all supplies ready and close at hand always makes for a smooth construction process. It also shows thought has been given to the character, and it eliminates extra trips to buy supplies during a moment of inspiration, or perspiration.

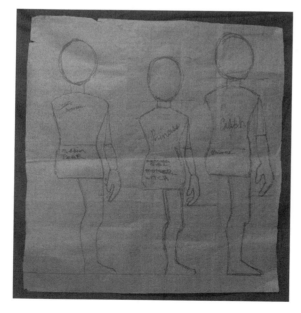

Fig. #2: Some examples of scale drawings for marionettes. This example shows the heights of three characters from a Fairyland show by Lewis Mahlmann.

About our marionette, Lewis Mahlmann suggests:

> *"This is the standard two foot (21 to 24 inches) cloth marionette pattern used at Fairyland. The puppet control illustrated has been found most practical for a two man "story telling" marionette show. Sketch out the undressed 21 to 24 inch puppet on butcher paper and follow that scale drawing for layout of the body parts as you go along. This is MOST important. It would be wise to draw out all the scale drawings first so you can compare the set of puppets as you make them. Always read all instructions before cutting."*

It is often a good idea with marionettes, to sketch out a scale drawing of the body of the puppet. A scale drawing does not have to be as detailed as the design. It basically shows the correct proportions of the puppet's body. This is particularly useful when the puppets in the show are of various heights and/or body structures. (See Fig #2) Our marionette patterns can easily be redrawn to match the specific heights of the desired puppets.

> **Note:** To resize the patterns, projecting them on a wall to the desired proportions is an easy way to do this. Or use the scale feature on most photocopiers. The patterns in this book will result in a 24" size marionette. Hand puppets are 20" in height.

THE HEAD

 As detailed in the last chapter, we chose and completed the style 'C' angular head for our marionette. Using a dowel which fits comfortably into the neck tube, cut a section 1-1/2" long. Attach a screw eye into the middle of the bottom then glue the dowel with white glue or hot glue, into the neck tube of the felt head. (See Fig #3)

Set the head aside for the moment. We'll come back to it later.

Fig. #3: Insert a screw eye into a dowel sized 1" x 1-1/2". Glue the dowel into the bottom of the finished head.

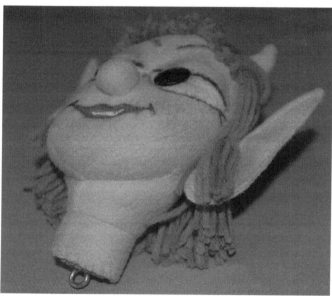

Fig. #4: The finished head with screw-eyed dowel in place.

MAKING THE MARIONETTE BODY

Step 1 - Creating the torso.

Trace the body pattern onto a piece of doubled muslin. Cut a 2″ long piece of 1/2″ dowel and in the center of it's length secure a screw eye like the one used in the neck of the head. (See Fig #4)

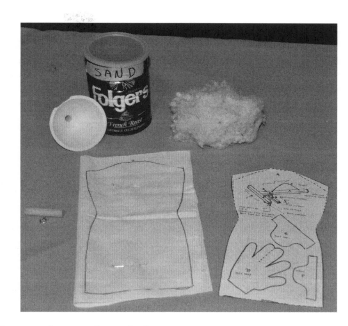

Fig. #4: The body pattern drawn on muslin.
Note: The screw-eyed 1/2" dowel at the left.

Machine sew the body leaving a 1" opening at the neck and the bottom unsewn. The opening at the top is for the screw eye to protrude through. Cut out and reverse the body. (See Fig #5)

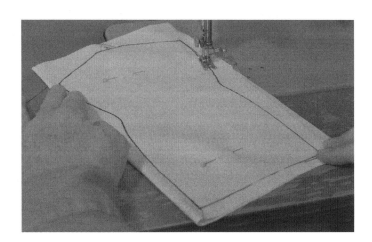

Fig. #5: Machine sew the body leaving an opening at the neck and at the bottom.

Stuff, with cotton or kapok, the top of the neck. Place the dowel into the body with the screw eye projecting through the neck opening. Stuff the upper part of the body, shaping the shoulders, and filling in around the dowel. Continue to firmly stuff the body to about three-quarters just below the waist. Add sand to give the torso the desired weight and stuff more kapok over the sand to about 1" from the muslin bottom.

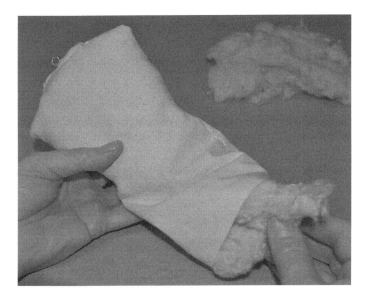

Fig. #6: Stuff the reversed body after placing the screw-eyed dowel at the top. Don't forget to add the sand.

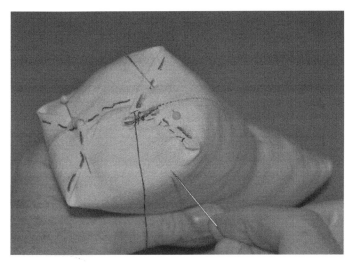

Fig. #7: Bottom of the body sewn closed like the side of a wrapped package.

Now fold, package wise, the balance of the muslin and sew closed. The bottom should look like the side of a wrapped package. (See Fig #6 -7) Set the body aside.

Step 2 - Making arms.

Trace and cut out from two (2) arm pieces. Choose the arm pattern you wish to use and cut two (2) arm pieces from muslin. Fold and pin each piece then machine sew from the top of the arm all the way down the side then across the bottom . Leave the top open. (See Fig #8 - 9) Turn the arms inside out. (See Fig # 9)

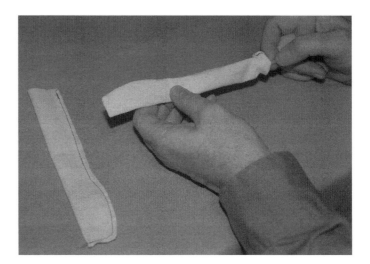

Fig. #8: Turn the sewn arms inside out.

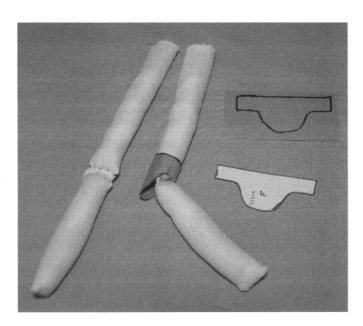

Fig. #9: Arms stuffed and elbow stitched.**Note**: the correct placement of the elbow cap on the arm and how it is used.

Put approximately one tablespoon of sand into the bottom of each the arm and stuff to just below the elbow joint. Locate where the elbow will bend and stitch across the arm. Stitch across again, 1/4" above the first stitching line. Lightly stuff the upper the arm, leaving 2" of material at the top for attaching to the body. (See Fig. #10)

Puck has a skin covering on his bare arm and an elbow will not look good. However, to make an elbow, cut two (2) elbow caps from thin cardboard. Place around the top section of the arm, just above the elbow joint (See Fig #10) so the rounded section reaches just below the stitched lines. Sew to the muslin. Leave the cardboard bottom unsewn so the arm will bend forward but not backward in an unnatural direction.

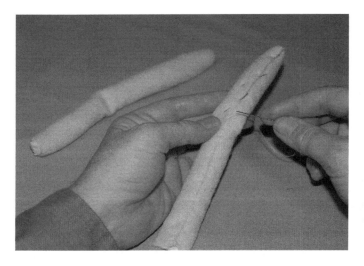

Fig. #10 Arms shown with skin covering added. **Note**: No elbow caps are used on Puck's covered arms.

Puck is to have bare arms so we will use a tight skin covering. Cut two (2) pieces measuring 9" x 3" from the flesh material. Wrap the skin around the arm, with the join at the back, pin and hand sew closed. Try to keep the stitches small and invisible. (See Fig # 11) Remember to keep the material just loose enough so the arm will bend at the stitched joint. Set aside when finished.

Step 3 - Sewing hands onto the arms.

Having chosen a hand pattern, follow the same instructions as described when building hands for a hand puppet. (See Fig #12)

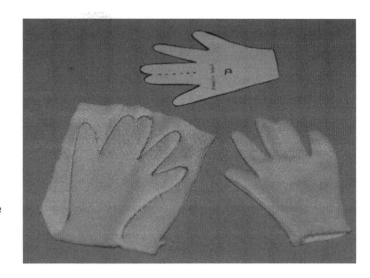

Fig. #11: Hand pattern (top) is stitched on the material (left) and turned inside out (right).

Note: It is a good idea when stuffing the hands, to add a teaspoon of sand to each for extra weight in the arms.

Pin the stuffed hands onto arms as shown and sew, with small stitches, around the base of the hand. Don't forget to add the wrapped string around the wrist of the puppet's hand to plump out the palm. (See Fig #12) Check back at the scale drawing to ensure the hands are placed at the right height for the puppet. Don't forget to sew them onto the arm with the thumbs facing forward.

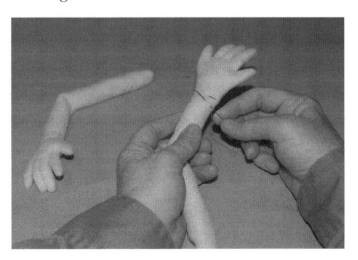

Fig. #12: Arms with hands sewn in place.

There are two patterns for the hands, narrower for ladies and wider for men. Set the arms aside when finished.

Step 4 - Making legs for the marionette.

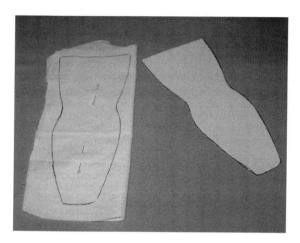

Fig. #13: Leg pattern traced on doubled muslin (left).

Cut two (2) of the leg pattern from muslin. (See Fig #13)

Fold the muslin pieces in half and pin the side of the leg. Leaving the top open, machine sew from the top of the leg to the bottom then across to the fold. Reverse the two legs. For a longer leg, add 2″ at the top of the pattern.

Note: The same leg pattern is used for male and female.

Pour the desired weight of sand into the bottom of the leg before stuffing. Stuff with kapok halfway up the leg to the bend. Like the arm, stitch across two times, with a 1/4″ gap, to create a bending knee joint for the final leg. Fill with more kapok leaving 2″ empty at the top. (See Fig #14)

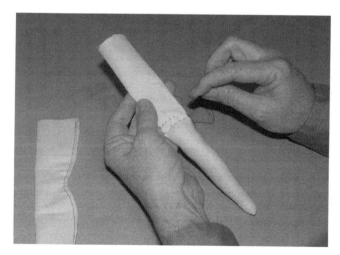

Fig. #14: When turned, and with bottom of the leg filled with sand and stuffing, stitch two lines across the knee.

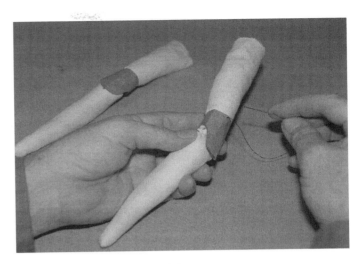

Fig. #15: Proper placement of knee caps.

We will use the knee cap pattern for our Puck figure. Cut two (2) out of light cardboard. Wrap the knee cap around the front of the leg and sew the top to the leg. The round area at the bottom, should fall below the stitched lines. Try bending the leg. Does the knee cap keep the leg from bending the wrong direction? (See Fig #15) Set aside when finished.

Step 5 - Making marionette shoes.

We have included two shoe patterns with the marionette patterns. The flat shoe was used with the hand puppet so this time we will focus on the less used "heel" type of shoe.

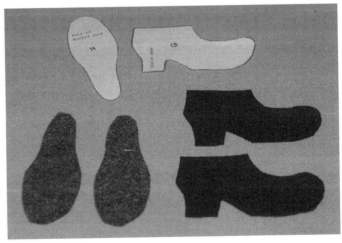

Fig. #16: Heel Shoe: Cut 2 of the soles and 4 of the side pieces..

Cut two (2) of heel sole, and four (4) of heel side out of the felt.
(See Fig #16) Remember, it is sometimes nice to cut the sole from a
different color felt as we have done with the example.

Sew one side of the shoe to the sole, starting at the middle of the
round front part and stopping at the middle of the back part.
Repeat with the other side of the shoe. Machine sew the two
profiles from the top front to the sole and from the top back all
the way down the heel to the sole. Our photo example shows a
stuffed and finished shoe on the left, and a sewn shoe, waiting to be
reversed, on the right. (See Fig #17) Reverse the shoe, and always
remember to check for weak stitches. Stuff the heel solidly with
kapok. We don't put a cardboard piece into this particular shoe. Go
ahead if you want. We feel it looks cuter just with the stuffing. If
cardboard is used, bend it in the shape of the sole, instep and heel.
It takes a bit of work, but is not difficult. Experiment and see what
can be created. Don't forget a little sand in the toe area.

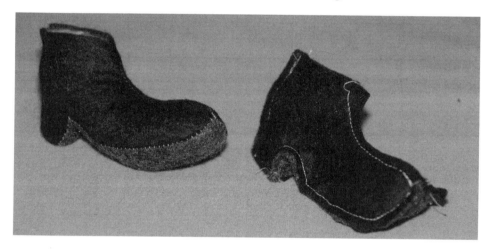

Fig. #17: A heeled
shoe

Place the finished legs into the stuffed, completed shoes. (See Fig
#18) Pin and see if the leg comfortably stands up when the shoe is
attached. Sew around the top of the shoe attaching it to the muslin
leg. There should be enough play for the foot to move freely when
the marionette walks. Pretend to walk the legs and feet around on
a smooth surface, and see if there is enough sand to weight the legs
and shoes properly.

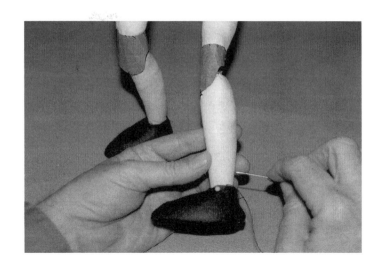

Fig. #18: Attaching the shoes to the legs.

Step 6 - Assembling the marionette body.

Before assembling the body parts, we suggest looking at the plans for the Marionette Costumer. Designed by Lewis Mahlmann, and recommended by puppet costumer Francis Oznowicz, it is a very useful tool for costuming marionettes. Easy to make, the Costumer allows the puppet to hang at work table height as the puppet is assembled and costumed. (See Fig #19)

Fig. #19: Marionette Costumer.

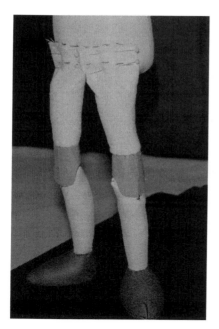

Fig. #20: Legs pinned to the puppet's torso which is hanging from the Marionette Costumer.

To assemble the marionette, pin the legs to bottom of the puppet torso. (See Fig #20) Since Puck is going to be wearing tights, we will just be pinning the legs for the moment. If pants are going to be created, go ahead and sew the legs on at this time. Remember to allow for a good sitting area at the bottom of the torso. After attaching the legs, loop a string from the screw eye in the neck so the puppet can stand comfortably on the Marionette Costumer.

Pin the arms on the sides of the puppet torso. The elbow should bend at the small of the waist area. (See Fig #21) Attach each arm to the slanted shoulder areas on body patterns.

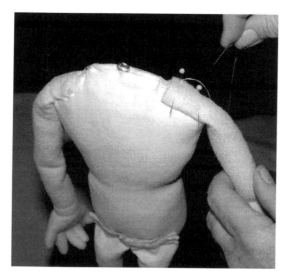

Fig. #21: Arm pinned to body with other stitched in place.

On assembling the body, Lewis Mahlmann suggests:

"Now that the marionette body is assembled, place it on the scale drawing and see if it is the same size you required. Remember men are usually a bit taller than women and children are shorter. If the figure needs a bust, stomach, rump of just a little filling out, now is the time to do it. Make little pillows and attach where needed. You might also use pieces of 1/4 inch foam rubber in the right places, shaping the body to size."

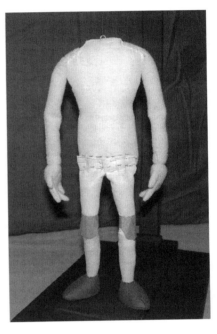

Fig. #22: Finished body awaiting costuming on the Marionette Costumer.

The puppet body is now completed! (See Fig #22) It is time to add the costuming and other colorful additions.

COSTUMING THE MARIONETTE

On costuming a marionette, Lewis Mahlmann suggests:
"It is always important to 'mock-up' the marionette clothing pieces before cutting the final fabric. Use cheap muslin in fitting the costume patterns, then cut into the final fabrics. Keep the costume loose in the right places so that nothing constricts the general movement of the marionette. This is why fitting in muslin first is MOST important. You only have to do one side of the figure to see if a jacket, sleeve or pants leg will work. Use soft materials like jerseys, light cottons, silks and the like. You can use felts and velvets if they don't restrict the movement. Do NOT put a hem in the bottom of jerseys for hems keep the jersey from falling in beautiful folds. Jersey does not fray. Perhaps white glue would be better to apply to end skirts on other fabrics if they will fall better."

Step 1 - Making a pair of simple pants.

Going back to our original design, notice Puck is wearing a pair of tights. Tights are similar to making pants with the exception they are form-fitting and hug to the puppet's torso and legs. Pants are made the same way as tights, only the pattern is wider along the thighs and ankles. Cut two (2) leg/tight patterns from the desired fabric. (See Fig #24)

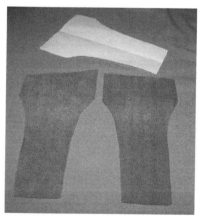

Fig. #23: Tight legs cut out of our chosen fabric.

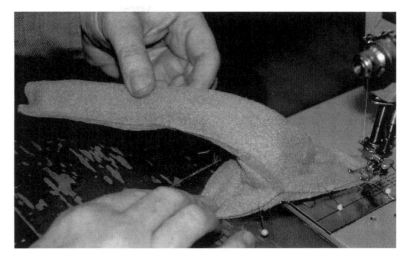

Fig. #24: Tight/pants leg being sewn on the machine.

Sew up each side of the tight legs from point A to point B. Reverse one of the legs and insert it into the other, unturned leg. (See Fig #25) Line up the front and back of tights and machine sew together.

Reverse the tights. As you will remember, we didn't sew the legs onto the torso of our assembled Puck. This was because we will put the tights on before the legs are attached to the body. Unpin one leg and insert it into one side of the tights. Pull the tights all the way down to where the shoe is sewn on the leg. Now pin the leg back on to the torso. Repeat this process with the other leg. Pull the tights up and see if the legs move freely back and forth. Adjust as needed. When satisfied, sew the legs to the torso as we did the arms. Now pull the tights up, pin around the torso, adjust them to the desired look and sew onto the torso and around the ankles at the bottom. (See Fig #26) Don't worry, the other parts of the elf shoe will cover the stitches.

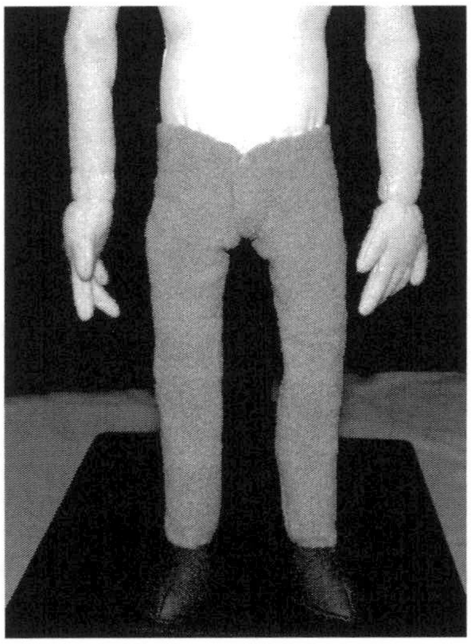

Fig. #25: Tights sewn onto the assembled body.

Note: A pair of pants would not be sewn at the bottom. The cuff hangs loosely.

Step 2 - Creating the shirt or tunic.

The marionette tunic will be made more like a real shirt this time. Our hand puppet tunic was placed on the body piece by piece while sewn. This time we will machine sew the sleeves directly to the tunic.

Fig. #26: Pieces ready to sew for the tunic shirt.

Cut from the tunic fabrics two (2) of the marionette sleeve pattern, two (2) of the tunic front, and one (1) of the tunic back. (See Fig #26)

Sew the tunic front pieces to the tunic back section at the shoulder seams (point A to point B) but do not sew along the side seams. (See Fig #27)

Fig. #27: Machine sew each tunic front to the back at the shoulder seams.

The curved area at the top of the pattern, where the sleeve fits into at the top of a shirt or bodice, is called an "armscye." Fold the sleeve in half and starting at the midpoint of the fold, pin it into the armscye beginning at the top of the shoulder. (See Fig #28) Pin down both side of the sleeve to the bottom of the armscye. Machine sew together. It should look like Fig #29. Do both sides of tunic.

Fig. #28: The sleeve is pinned to the tunic at the armscye.

Fig. #29: This is how the tunic/shirt should look when the sleeve is sewn into place.

Pin together then sew the tunic's side seams. Starting at the tip at the bottom of the sleeve, sew up to the armpit, and then down to the bottom of the tunic/shirt. (See Fig #30) Reverse when finished.

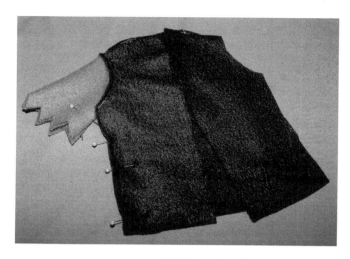

Fig. #30: Tunic/Shirt pinned and ready to sew the undersleeve and side seam.

With both sleeves sewn in and the tunic closed on the sides, place the garment on the puppet body. Pin the front closed and hand sew. Sew the bottom of the tunic/shirt to the pants which are already on. (See Fig #31) If Puck had a regular shirt on, separate cuffs and collar would be added as well as the buttons of choice. See a real shirt for ideas.

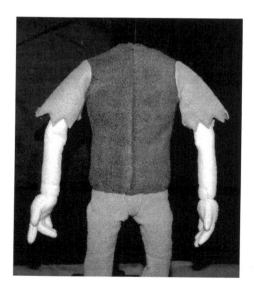

Fig. #31: Puck's tunic sewn onto the body.

Using our original patterns from the hand puppet for Puck's tunic bottom, collar and boot sections, create those pieces for this costume. The measurement this time for Pucks belt is: 1" x 12-1/2". Attach these pieces to the completed body. For proper placement of Puck's collar, see the next step. Be sure to gather Puck's tunic bottom when sewing in place.

Step 3 - Attaching the head to the marionette body.

Gather the elfin collar around the base of the Marionette head and sew in place. (See Fig #33)

Fig. #32: Sew Puck's collar to his neck.

To attach head, open one of the screw eyes and loop it through the other one. Close the screw eye after the two are linked. (See Fig #33)

Fig. #33: Hook the two neck screw eyes together and close tightly.

Attach a string to each side of the puppet head and form a loop to hang the completed puppet from the Marionette Costumer. It is ready for stringing!

Fig. #345: Puck is costumed and ready for stringing.

MAKING AND STRINGING THE CONTROL

There are many, many different types of marionette controls. The one we favor at Fairyland is a simple 9-string wooden control. It has a T-bar for making the puppet walk and bend, a pivoting head bar to give action to the head, and two small rods to make the hands move.

This is a great control because one person can easily work two puppets at the same time. Since all our shows have two people manipulating, this control allows for four puppets to move at once.

From 3/4" x 1/2" wood stock, cut the following pieces:
1 - Main bar control @ 8-1/2 "
1 - Leg bar @ 6"
1 - Head bar @ 5"

From 1/4" dowel cut:
2 - Hand dowels @ 4"

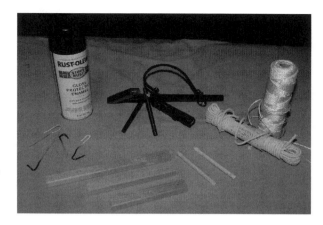

Fig. #35: A finished marionette control surrounded by items need to make another.

Sand all the edges to make them smooth to the touch and smooth the sides of the control for a good grip. Drill the following holes for each of the control pieces:

Head Bar - Drill a 1/4″ hole in the center of the piece.

Main Control Bar - Drill two (2) 1/4″ holes 2-1/2″ in from the front and 2-1/2″ from the back through the top of the main bar. **On the side** of the main bar drill a 1/8″ hole 1-1/2″ from the front.

Hand Bars - Drill a 1/8″ hole at the top each of the hand bar and a 1/16″ hole at the bottom.

Leg Bar - Glue and nail the center of the leg to the front of the Main Bar wood piece, creating a "T" bar. Be sure to sand all the rough edges around the holes. There should be four (4) separate pieces of the control.

It is time to paint the control pieces. A good practice when making puppets, is to have a clothesline running across some area of the workshop. It is used for hanging puppet pieces which have been painted and need to dry. Pieces of strong wire can be bent into S-hooks of assorted lengths to suspend painted items. If the piece being painting has a hole in it which the S-hook will fit through (such as the hand bars), great! If not, twist a small screw eye into the end of one of the cut wood pieces. The piece can be hung up to dry from this, and afterwards the screw eye can be removed for other uses. Select a desired spray paint color and evenly spray each of the four control parts. Hang from clothesline to dry. (See Fig #36)

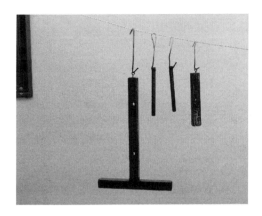

Fig. #36: Painted control parts, hanging from wire S-hooks, on a clothesline.

To assemble the control parts, cut a piece of supple clothesline rope 22" in length. This is going to be the main control rope. A thin, supple rope-string, 8" in length and easily tied will hold the hand bars. When putting rope or string through the holes on the control wood, it is good practice to wrap a small piece of masking tape on the end so it will thread easily through the holes and not fray.

Tie a large knot at the bottom of the 22" rope piece. Pass the rope through the head bar, and tie another knot approx. 1" above the head bar on the rope. Pass the rope through the front hole on the "T" bar and tie another knot close to the hole on top. This will keep the head bar from slipping down. (See Fig #37) Approximately 7-1/2" above the last knot, tie another knot. Slip the rope through the "T" bar from the top and tie a final knot at the bottom of the control bar. The 22" piece should now have a total of five (5) knots in it. Cut off the loose end.

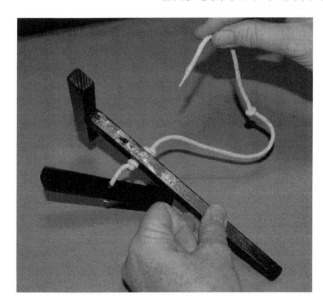

Fig. #37: Inserting the main hanging rope into the marionette control. **Note**: Masking tape on end of rope.

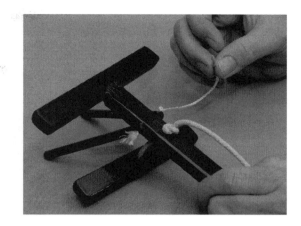

Fig. #38: Attaching the hand bars to the "T" bar.

Tie a couple of knots at the end of the 8" piece of thin rope-string. and thread it through one of the hand bars then through the side of the "T" bar. Slip the other hand bar on the other side and tie off with a couple of knots. Make sure the hand bars are knotted snugly against the sides of the "T" bar. (See Fig #38) Glue all knots shut.

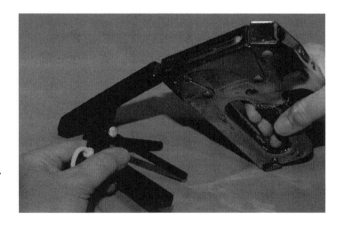

Fig. #39: Putting staples in the ends of the control · for attaching puppet strings.

The next decision is whether to use staples or screw eyes for attaching the marionette strings to the controls. Each has its own advantages and disadvantages. We use staples at Fairyland. Screw eyes with the strings attached can be removed from the control if the puppet gets tangled. However, screw eyes tend to catch other strings and cause many headaches. With staples, just tie the string off and there is no chance of the staple catching in other strings. However, staples cannot be easily removed to untangle a mess if needed. Choose wisely. Staples, or screw eyes, are placed on either end of the leg and head bars, and at the back of the "T' bar. (See Fig #39)

Fig. #40: Puck lying on the table with all the strings attached to the body.

At Fairyland, we attach all the needed strings to the puppet figure before connecting them to the actual control. We measure the length of our strings, add 6 extra inches, and attach them in each of the following places on our marionette: Each side of the head (ear level), both shoulders, the rear or rump, at each kneecap and finally on the wrist of each arm. Nine (9) strings in all. This is all accomplished while the puppet is lying down. (See Fig #40) For stringing marionettes we use a durable carpet thread from Coats Co. that is a 3 oz black braided nylon. It is easy to tie and moves well. Fishing line is constrictive, and most often used for heavier marionettes.

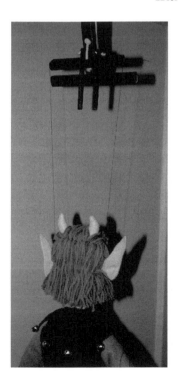

Fig. #41: Head strings attached to the control.

Hang the control, on a nail or hook, and tie off the head strings to either side of the head bar. Make sure the strings are even and the head bar is parallel to the leg bar in the front. (See Fig #41 & 42)

Now attach the other strings in the following order:

> **Note:** When tying off strings, always tie three (3) knots. Add even two (2) more for safety.

Shoulder strings: Tie off the shoulder strings to the back end of the "T' bar. Make sure the shoulders are even. After stringing, move the head up and down and make sure the shoulder strings allow the head to move freely.

Rear or rump string: Attach the rear string at the same location as the shoulder strings. There should now be three (3) strings coming from this location. This string will help balance the puppet and help him to bow and move his head.

Leg strings: Tie off a leg string to either side of leg bar. Make sure the strings are even and the leg is not raised off the ground when the figure is hanging. Test walk the puppet and make sure all strings are in alignment.

Hand strings: Finally, we attach the hand strings through the small holes drilled in each of the hand bars. When stringing the hands, we usually raise the hands a little so the arm is not completely at rest by the puppet's side. This also allows for a better hand raise when lifting the bars during operation.

Fig. #42: Correct placement of strings on the marionette control.

<u>Specialty strings:</u> Finally we add any specialty strings. In this case, we put a small loop in Puck's mouth, and then ran a string from the Pan Pipes, through the mouth loop, and up to the control. The string is attached to the front of the "T" bar for easy access. When pulled, Puck can play the pipes.

Practice making the puppet come to life and enjoy what you can do just by pulling a few strings. (See Fig #43)

Fig. #43: Puck is ready for performance.

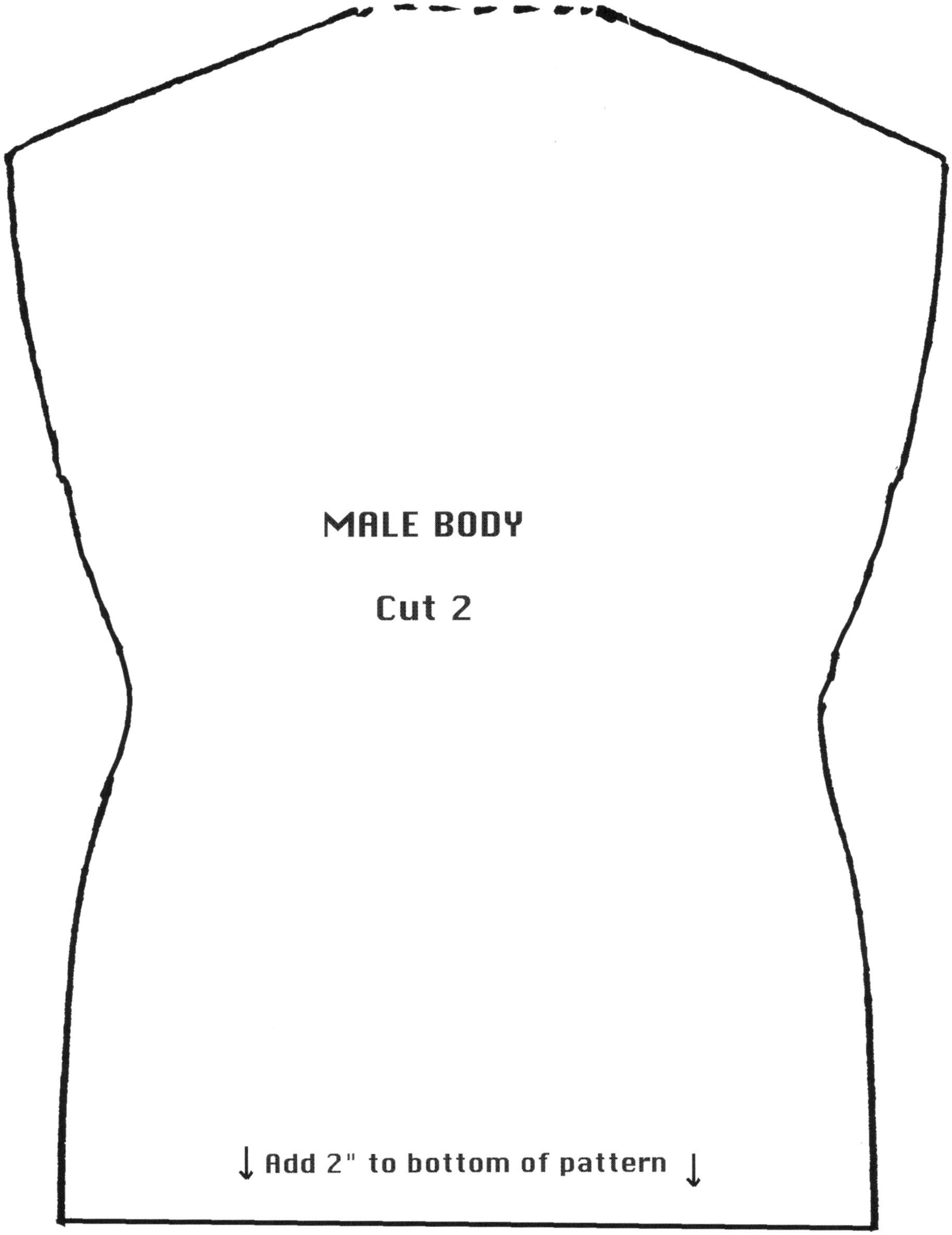

MALE BODY

Cut 2

↓ Add 2" to bottom of pattern ↓

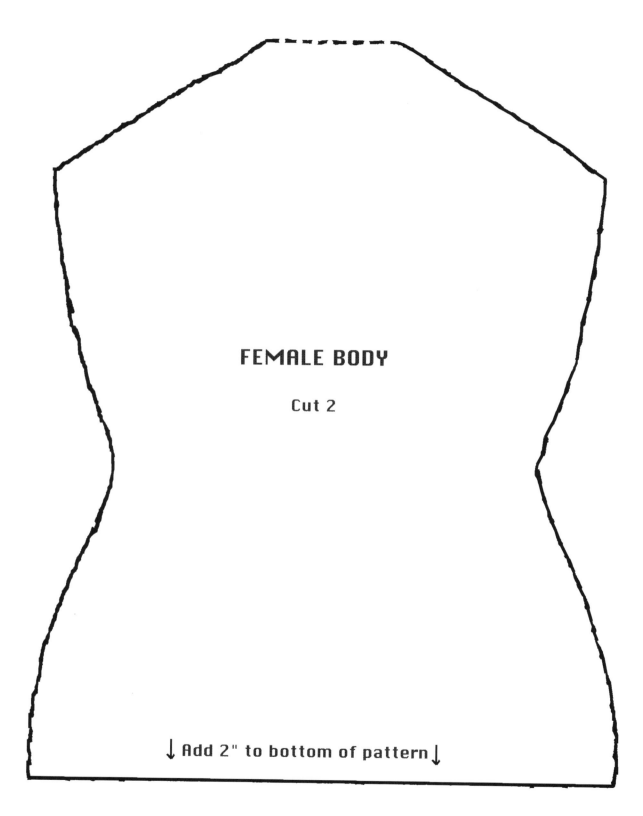

FEMALE BODY

Cut 2

↓ Add 2" to bottom of pattern ↓

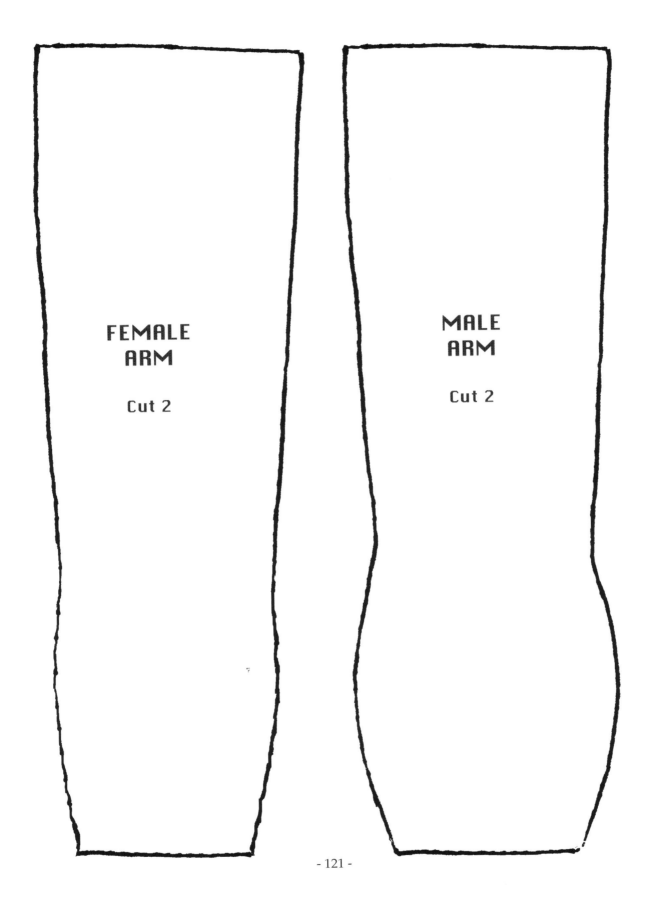

FEMALE
ARM

Cut 2

MALE
ARM

Cut 2

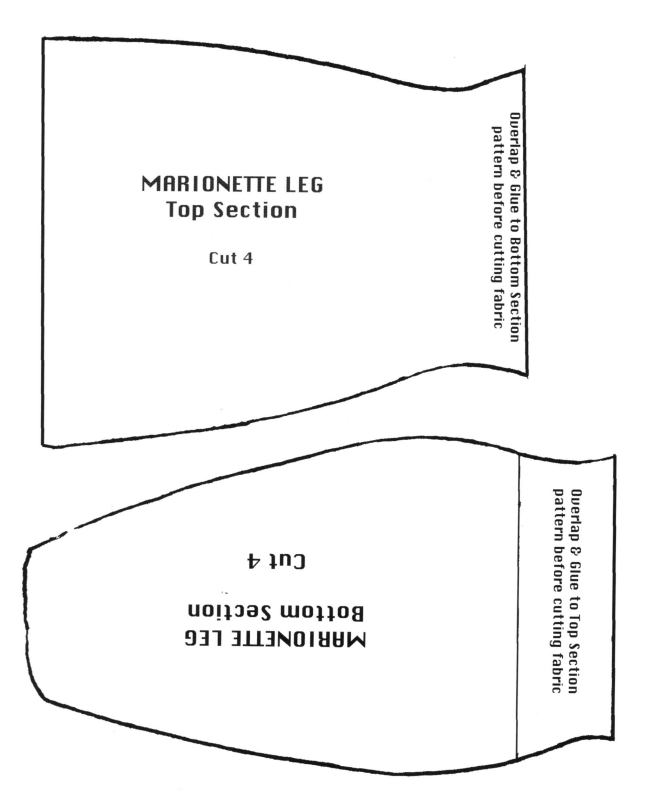

MARIONETTE LEG
Top Section

Cut 4

Overlap & Glue to Bottom Section
pattern before cutting fabric

MARIONETTE LEG
Bottom Section

Cut 4

Overlap & Glue to Top Section
pattern before cutting fabric

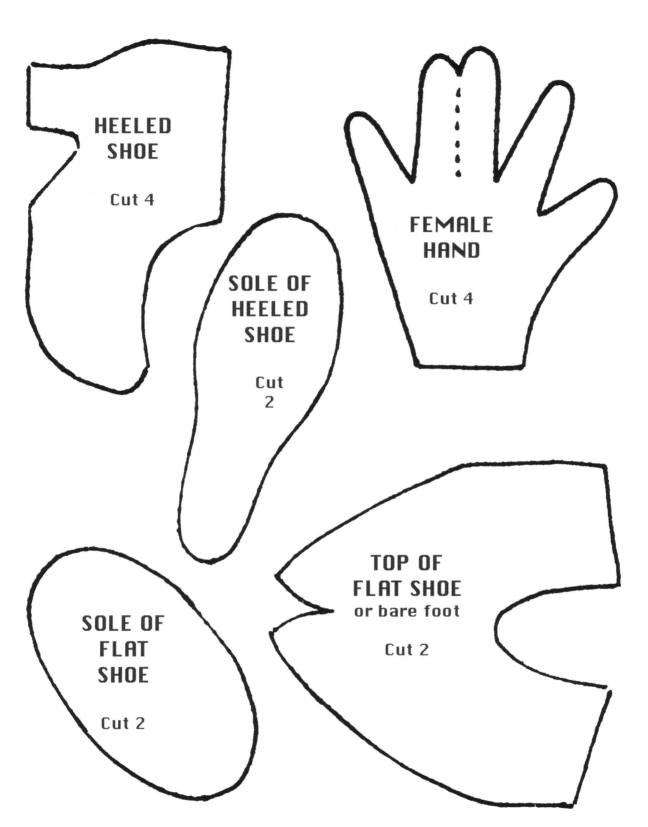

HEELED SHOE

Cut 4

SOLE OF HEELED SHOE

Cut 2

FEMALE HAND

Cut 4

SOLE OF FLAT SHOE

Cut 2

TOP OF FLAT SHOE
or bare foot

Cut 2

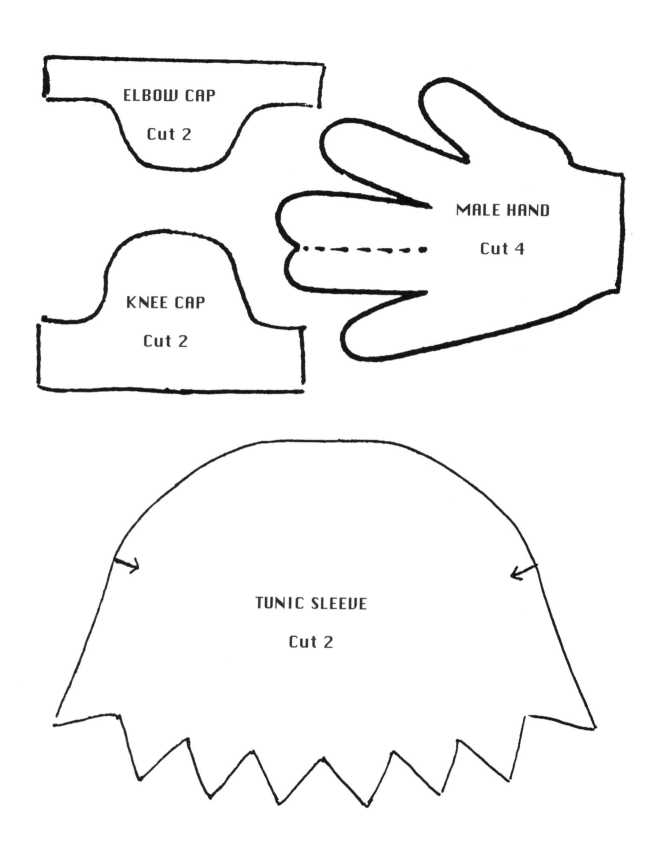

ELBOW CAP

Cut 2

MALE HAND

Cut 4

KNEE CAP

Cut 2

TUNIC SLEEVE

Cut 2

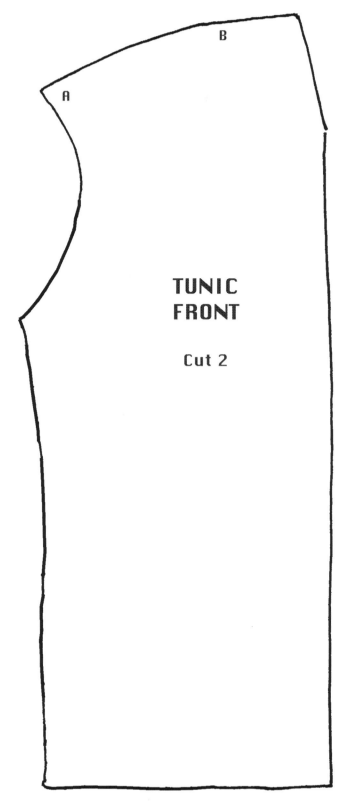

TUNIC
FRONT

Cut 2

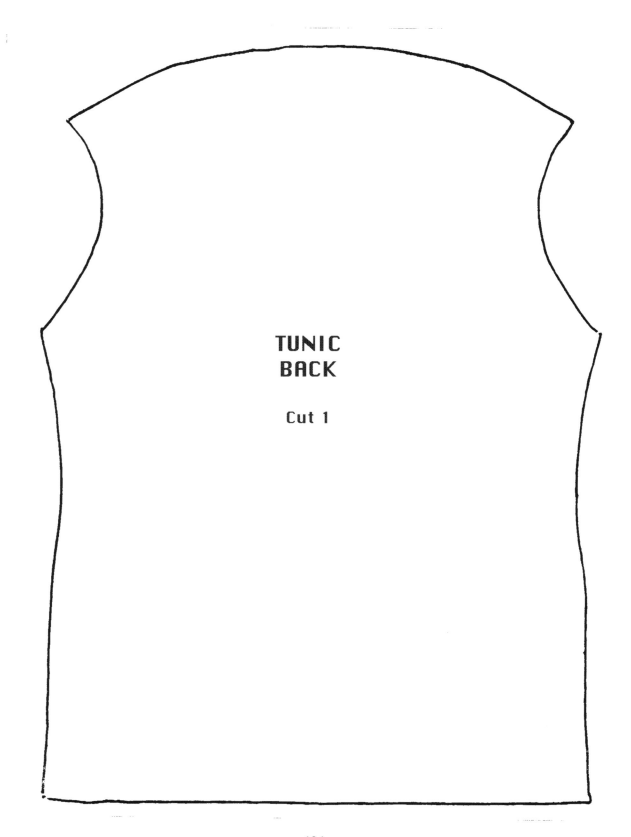

TUNIC
BACK

Cut 1

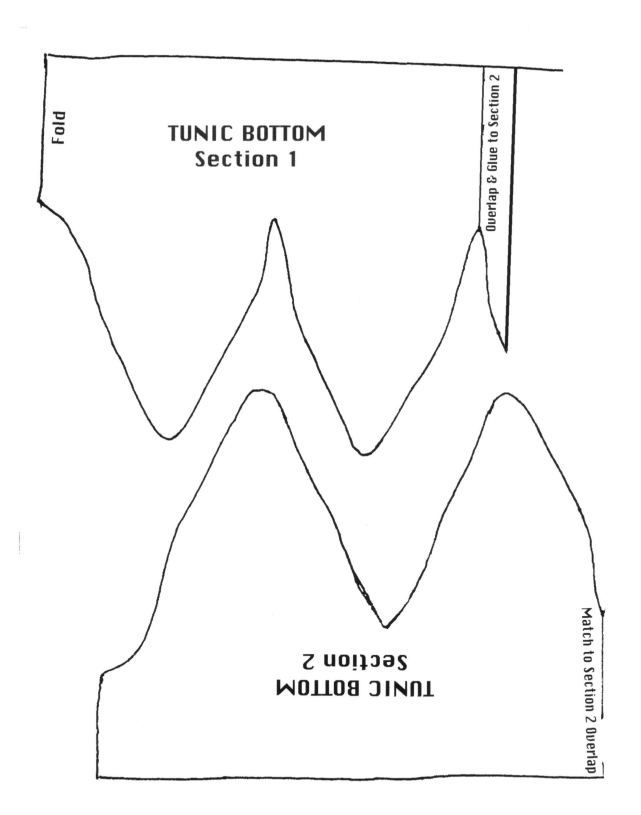

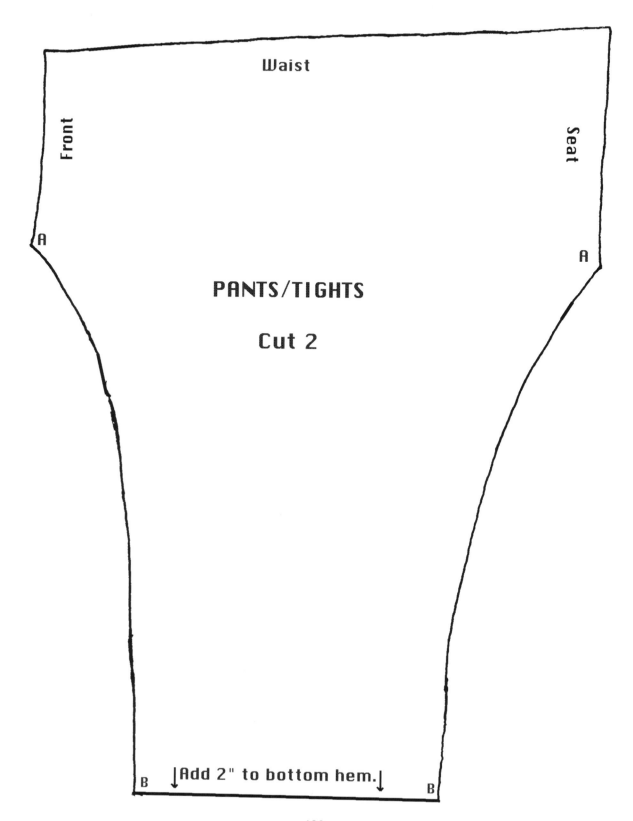

Waist

Front

Seat

A

A

PANTS/TIGHTS

Cut 2

B   ↓ Add 2" to bottom hem. ↓   B

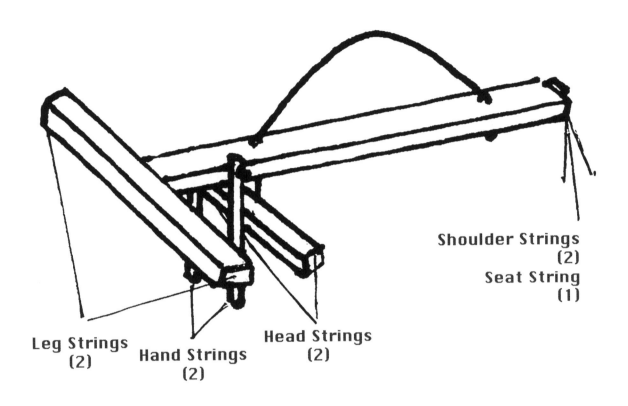

**Shoulder Strings
(2)
Seat String
(1)**

**Leg Strings
(2)**

**Hand Strings
(2)**

**Head Strings
(2)**

Main Bar = 8-1/2"
Leg Bar = 6"
Head Bar = 5"
Hand Bars = 4"

Costumer

IT'S EASY TO CONSTRUCT A "COSTUMER" FOR DRESSING YOUR PUPPETS
BASED ON THIS DESIGN BY LEWIS MAHLMANN, OAKLAND, CALIFORNIA.
Illustration by Maury Haykin, New Jersey.

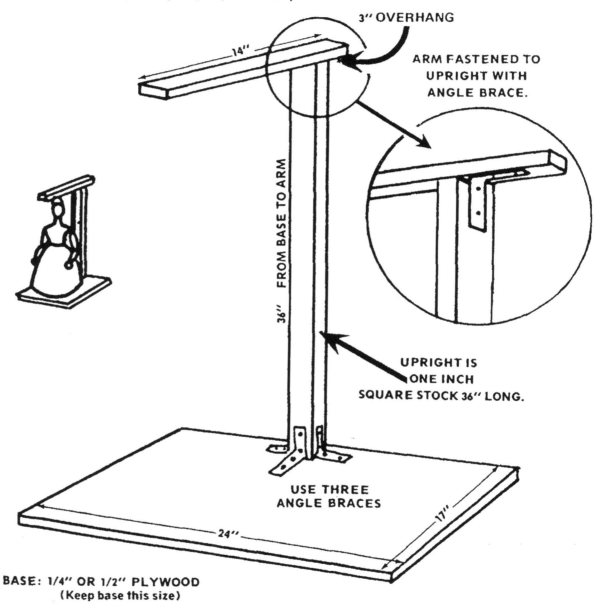

3" OVERHANG

ARM FASTENED TO
UPRIGHT WITH
ANGLE BRACE.

14"

36" FROM BASE TO ARM

UPRIGHT IS
ONE INCH
SQUARE STOCK 36" LONG.

USE THREE
ANGLE BRACES

24"

17"

BASE: 1/4" OR 1/2" PLYWOOD
(Keep base this size)

CHAPTER 5: CREATING A ROD PUPPET

The third and last type of puppet we will make is a Rod Puppet. So named because the figure is worked by wire rods and dowels connected to the body of the puppet. The most basic rod puppet is built just like a marionette. The difference is, instead of strings, there is a 1/2" dowel running up through the bottom of the body and glued into the head. Washers at the top and bottom of the torso, with nails holding them in place, allow the puppet's head to turn from side to side. Wire rods are then attached to the hands and worked from below. This type of puppet has the most limited movement on stage. It is often stiff and doesn't move at the waist.

The patterns we will use for our rod puppet have been specially adapted to allow the rod figure to have movement at the waist, as well as action in the head and arms. It's almost a hand/rod puppet. This figure can move gracefully on stage and gives more of an illusion of life to the audience. Legs and feet can be added to the puppet, but for our purposes they will be omitted.

Rod puppets are used for stories requiring a complete puppet figure on stage which needs to work from below the stage level. Rod puppets are also useful when there are a lot of characters on stage but a lack of puppeteers' hands. The puppets can be placed into holders and still animated while standing in place.

Once again, here is a suggested list of items needed for making a rod puppet:

1) Felt or fleece colors for hands and head
2) Bleached muslin for creating the body sleeve
3) Chosen materials and trims for costume
4) Threads: sewing and/or embroidery for above materials
5) Choice of stuffing for body parts

6) Yarns or furs for wigs
7) Faceted buttons for eyes
8) Small make up selection of eye shadows for face details
9) Bendable, thin cardboard for neck and wig templates
10) Pipe Cleaner for fingers of hands
11) Heavy cardboard/wood, 1/8" thick, for shoulder piece
12) Light, durable cardboard for chest & palm inserts
13) 1 - 12" piece of 1/2" wood dowel

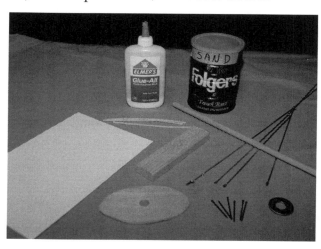

Fig. #1: Some of the new materials used in a rod puppet. **Note**: Wire umbrella stays.

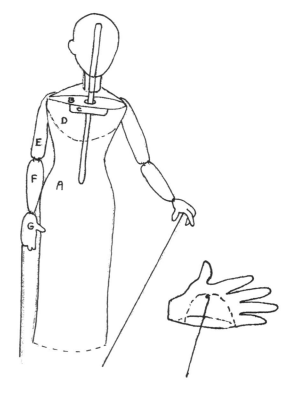

Fig. #2: Design by Lewis Mahlmann of a Fairyland rod puppet.
A - Body sleeve
B - Shoulder
C - Neck support
D - Chest
E - Upper Arm
F - Lower Arm
G - Hand

14) 1 - piece of wood 3" x 1-1/4" x 3/4" for body neck support and a 5/8" drill bit
15) 1 - 1/2" washer
16) 1 - 1-3/4" finishing nail
17) 1/4" doweling for hand control rods
18) 2 - Umbrella stays or wire coat hanger for hand rods
19) And of course....scissors, pins, needles, masking tape, marking pens, sand, and paper for extra patterns (as needed)

THE HEAD AND CONTROL ASSEMBLY

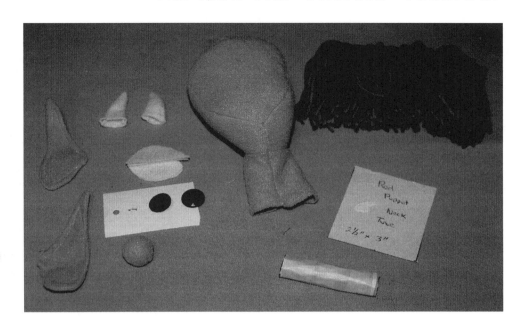

Fig. #3: Felt head with pre-sewn facial features ready to be assembled.
Note: The new measurement for the neck tube: 2-1/2 by 3".

Step 1 - Cutting out the head pieces. Using the style 'C' Angular felt puppet head.

Again, for this rod puppet I have used my favorite, the style 'C' Angular puppet head pattern. But the styles 'A' or 'B' head patterns can also be used. Always remember: if we do a step that you are unsure of, look back in past chapters since we have used many of those puppet making steps over and over again. (See Fig #3)

Step 2 - Assembling the head pieces.

The head is assembled like the previous marionette puppet. The only change is the construction of the neck tube which is made from a 2-1/2" x 3" piece of cardboard. Instead of finger sized, the

Fig. #4 Finished rod puppet head placed on the end of the control dowel. It is not yet glued in place.

diameter of the neck tube should be slightly larger than 1/2". Stuff the head, leaving room for the insertion of the cardboard tube. Install tube in neck and add stuffing around the tube to fill out the puppet's neck. With a gather stitch, pull in the circumference of the neck material and sew to the smaller tube. Don't forget to adjust the height of the neck to suit the desired puppet. As Lewis has suggested, always check the puppet against a scale drawing.

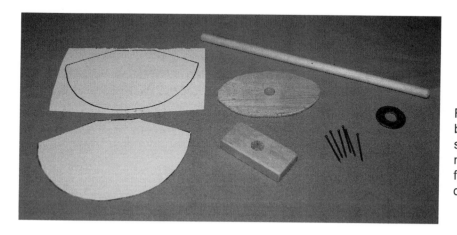

Fig. #5: Control pieces: cardboard cutouts for chest, wood sections for the shoulder and neck support. A 1/2" washer, finishing nails, and 1/2" wood dowel.

Finish the head by adding the hair, nose, eyes, ears, horns and makeup. The 12" long piece of 1/2" dowel fits snugly into the head. (See Fig #4)

Step 3 - Making the rod puppet control mechanism .

Cut the two (2) chest pieces out of an 8″ x 5″ piece of pliable cardboard. Make sure to use the correct chest pattern for the gender of the body being made. Set the cardboard pieces aside.

From the 1/2″ dowel cut a 12″ piece. Drill a small hole in the center of the dowel which will allow the 1-3/4″ finishing nail to fit tightly in. Place the nail through the dowel. Place the 1/2″ washer over the dowel to rest atop the nail.

From a 3″ x 1-14″ x 3/4″ thick piece of wood, cut out the neck support. Drill the hole of the pattern using a 5/8″ drill bit. (same size as hole) Cut out the shoulder piece pattern from light wood or a very heavy cardboard. This piece, before cutting, is 8″ x 5″. Drill the hole in the designated area as was done with the neck support. Now line up the holes and glue and nail the two pieces together.

Fig. #6: Completed head control mechanism for a rod puppet.

> **Note:** The two pieces should swivel easily on the 1/2″ dowel. Place the finished section onto the dowel. For completed piece see Fig #6.

Making the Rod Puppet Body

Step 1 - Creating the body sleeve and chest pieces.

Trace the desired body pattern onto a piece of folded muslin. Remember to add 10-1/2" to the body pattern in order to make the rod puppet body long enough to cover the puppeteer's forearm. (See Fig #7) Sew the body leaving an opening at the top and bottom of the pattern. Cut out - but do not turn it inside out for strength. Leave a healthy muslin edge around cut body.

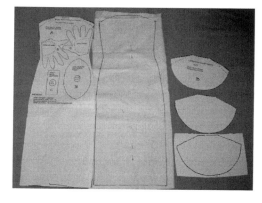

Fig. #7: Rod puppet body pattern drawn on muslin with 10-1/2"added to body length.

With masking tape, join together the two sides of the shoulder areas of the chest pieces. Bend the cardboard to make sure the control mechanism will fit into the bottom section of this cardboard piece. See Fig #8 for completion of chest pieces. Paint white glue onto both sides of the chest piece. This step is easier if the cardboard is placed inside the muslin body and then glue is painted onto the cardboard from the neck opening. Press the muslin to the glued areas and make sure the cardboard fits snugly into the body.

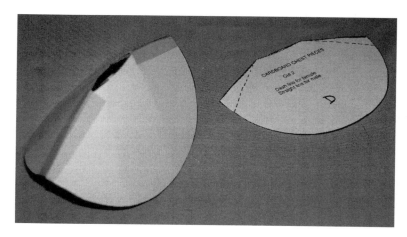

Fig. #8: Rod puppet chest piece taped together at the shoulders.

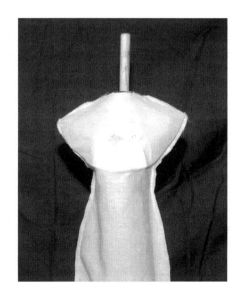

Fig. #9: Muslin body with chest and control placed inside.

The next step is a little tricky. When the glue has properly set, take the head control assembly and insert it into the bottom of the puppet body. The shoulder section should just fit into the bottom of the cardboard chest piece, with the dowel sticking out the top of the body. (See Fig #9) Securely glue the chest pieces onto the edge of the oval shoulder piece. The dowel and washer can be removed for this step. To insure the piece will stay in place, put a staple on the front and back of the body holding the chest piece to the shoulder section.

> **Note:** Make sure the dowel, when placed into the shoulder control, is centered with the muslin body.

The mid waist tends to gather into an hour glass shape because of the chest piece. In order to give more shape and strength to the body, we have included an optional skin top piece. (See Fig #10) This gives a better look to the completed puppet and can be covered with clothing. For the top body skin pattern, fold a piece of fabric and trace the outline. Machine sew, leaving an opening at the top and bottom, cut it out and turn inside out. Place over the muslin body (Fig #10) and sew the bottom to the muslin torso. Glue the neck opening at the top. The next step is to securely glue the finished head onto the top of the dowel. Make sure the neck lightly fits into the finished chest piece. Hot glue is best for this step. After it is glued, the head should move easily at the neck from side to side by turning the dowel inside the body.

Fig. #10: Rod puppet body with optional top skin and head in place.

Step 2 - Adding Pants to the rod puppet body.

Pants are done just like we did with the hand puppet in Chapter Two. Trace the rod puppet pants pattern onto a doubled piece of selected fabric. Sew up the two sides, leaving the top and bottom open. Cut the sewn piece out of the fabric. Insert the pants, good sides facing, into the bottom of the puppet body. Pin and machine sew around the bottom. Pull the pants out of the bottom of the body. The rough seam is now on the outside. Pull the pants up and over the muslin body, turning them the correct way. Now machine sew a seam around the bottom of the puppet body once again. To finish it off, hand sew the top of the pants to the completed body at the top. (See Fig #11) For a pictorial example of this step, please see making pants for the hand puppet.

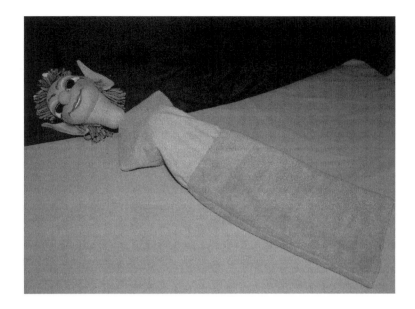

Fig. #11: Pants sewn onto the rod puppet body.

Step 3 - Making rod puppet arms.

Trace the rod puppet arms, top and bottom, onto a folded piece of muslin. Once again, make sure to use the correct arm gender for the body type: male or female. (See Fig #12)

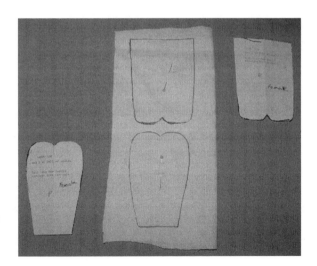

Fig. #12: Top and bottom rod puppet arms traced onto muslin.

Cut the arms out of the muslin, creating two (2) top and two (2) bottom arm sections. Fold the lower arm sections down the middle and sew across the bottom and up the side to the top. Fold the upper arm sections and sew down the side from the top to the bottom and then across to the fold. When finished and turned inside out, the rounded sections create the elbow area of the arm. (See Fig #13) Stuff the lower part of the arm to midpoint, then add a teaspoon of sand, and finish stuffing. Stuff the upper arm, leaving 1-1/2" un-stuffed at the top for sewing to body. Join the rounded sections and sew together with two (2) strong stitches. (See also Fig #13)

Place the completed arms to the side.

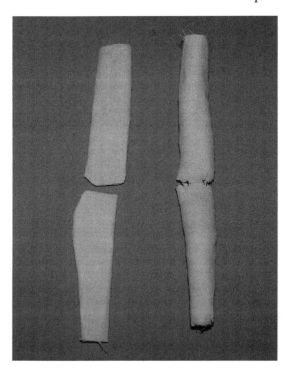

Fig. #13: Rod puppet arm turned inside out (left, and completed (right).

Step 4 - Creating hands and attaching to body.

Trace the chosen hand pattern onto to the skin fabric. Starting at the outside bottom of the little finger, sew on the line all the way to around to below the thumb at the wrist. See Fig #14 to see how the hand is machine sewn. Make a pattern for the cardboard palm inserts which will be placed inside the hand. The dotted lines inside the rod puppet hand patterns show the insert pattern as well as where the inserts will be placed. Trace and cut out four (4) palm sections out of light cardboard. (See Fig #14)

Trim and turn the hands inside out. Next stuff tightly, the thumb and four fingers, all the way to the "V" section.

Note: Don't forget to add pipe cleaners if the fingers are to be bent into different positions. Glue a cardboard palm insert to each inside surface of the hands, then hand sew the bottom of the palm cardboard to the open flesh material of the hand. (See Fig #15) Add stuffing as desired to fill out where the cardboard meets the fingers.

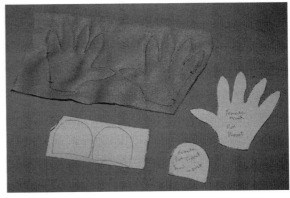

Fig. #14: Hand pattern (right) stitched on flesh material (upper left). Palm insert drawn onto cardboard.

Fit each hand over the wrist area on the muslin arms. Pin, and sew in place with tight stitches. When attached, the palm slot should be close to the muslin arm. See Fig #16 for what it should look like. With both hands attached to the arms, an outer skin can be made. Cut two (2) strips 8-1/2" x 3" of skin fabric and following the same steps used in adding skin to the marionette arm, sew the fabric down the underside of the arm and to the hand itself. (See Fig #16)

When both arms have been finished, pin them on the slanted shoulders of the puppet's torso. Be sure the hands hang properly at mid-waist. Sew the arms to the torso of the rod puppet. (See Fig #17) The rod puppet's body is now completed and ready for costuming.

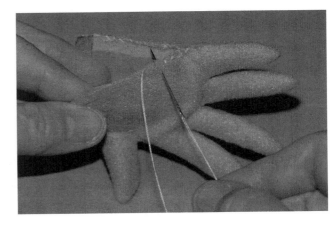

Fig. #15: Stitching the palm insert to bottom of hand after the insert has been glued into the stuffed hand.

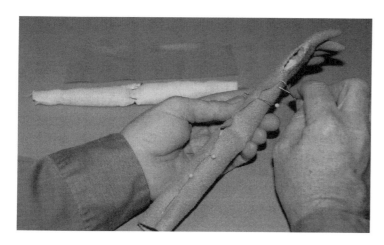

Fig. #16: Arm skin being sewn onto the completed arm and hand.

Fig. #17: The completed arm and hand is attached to the shoulder.

Step 1 - Making a shirt/tunic for Puck.

The tunic for the rod puppet Puck is made just like the tunic for the marionette Puck. The only difference is the pattern sizes. Trace the patterns onto the desired tunic fabrics. These will include two (2) sleeves, one (1) back of tunic & two (2) side tunic pieces. Sew the pieces on the machine as explained in chapter 4. (See Fig 18)

Fig. #18: Puck's completed tunic and the patterns used.

Fit the tunic onto the rod puppet body. Close the front of the tunic with pins, and also pin the bottom of the tunic around the torso of the puppet. Hand sew the bottom of the tunic to the body, and the front of the tunic closed. Make sure when pinning that the body can bend and move comfortably. (See Fig #19)

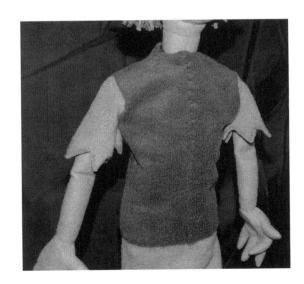

Fig. #19: Puck's tunic top is sewn in place and ready for the collar, bottom and belt..

Fig. #20: Puck's collar, belt, pipes, and tunic bottom are ready for application.

Return to Chapter 2 and find the patterns for Puck's bottom of tunic, and collar. Re-create these pieces for the rod puppet costume. The measurement for Puck's belt this time is: 1" x 15". Don't forget his pan pipes if needed! (See Fig #20) Sew each of these items onto the puppet. See Chapter 2 for complete details. We haven't used legs for this figure but they can be made from the patterns for the hand puppet or marionette legs. Don't forget his shoes - using proper patterns.

Step 2 - Making rod arm controls for Puck.

The puppet is almost finished. We still need to make control rods to work the arms. Umbrella stays which are removed from an old umbrella work best for us. They are very strong and already have a hole at the end of the rod for sewing into the hand. If you don't have an old umbrella, use cut coat hangers. Bend to straighten then form a small curled loop at the end for sewing into the hand.

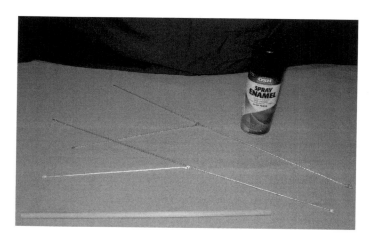

Fig. #21: Two umbrella stays, 1/4" dowel, and spray paint ready for making hand rods.

Carefully remove the umbrella stays from the umbrella mechanism. Use wire cutters to remove the nylon top and to cut the wire holding the stays to the center of the umbrella handle. When finished, they will look like the ones in Fig #21. With pliers, pull the shorter metal rod off of the longer one and discard.

Cut two (2) 5" lengths of 1/4" wood dowel, Drill a 1-1/2" deep hole, slightly smaller than the metal rod into the end of each dowel. Glue the rod in place and then spray paint to the color scheme. (See Fig #22) The finished rods should be about 20" in length.

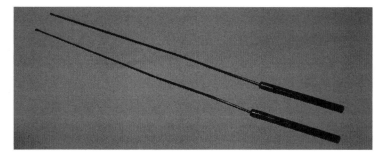

Fig. #22: Two finished hand rods ready to be sewn onto the puppet

Using a strong, light-colored carpet thread, string a needle which can pass through the hole in the control rod and knot the end of the thread. Pass the needle through the hole and catch the thread knotting it onto the end of the rod. Pass through the metal hole three (3) more times for strength. The thread is now tied onto the end of the metal stay. Pass the needle up between the cardboard and out at the base of the wrist in the arm. (See Fig #23) Insert the arm rod into the hand area until the tip is at the top of the wrist. Push the needle through the hole, from the outside, once again catching the end of the metal rod. Do this a couple of more times for strength and tie off the thread. Trim off excess thread. The rod should now control the arm, and hang down the side of the hand when not in use. Do this on the other arm.

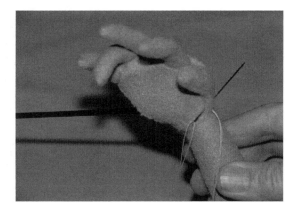

Fig. #23: Attaching the hand rod. **Note**: Needle pushing through the top of the wrist and passing through the enclosed hole on the hand rod.

Fig. #24: A finished Puck rod puppet.

The rod puppet is complete. Try manipulating it. See how the head and hands work together to control the body movement, and the arm allows for bending at the waist. (See Fig #24) You've made a simple, sophisticated rod puppet.

There are many different types of rod puppets, from very simple figures, to complicated, mechanized creations. The rod puppet we have made is very much like a hand puppet.

The most common form of this puppet is made in a nature similar to our marionette. The torso of the figure is held onto a rod running through the puppet by the washers at the bottom and neck of the body. You can make the puppets head move side to side (as we did with this one) or you can glue the head permanently in place, with no movement. This type of figure can then be placed in wooden holders on the puppet stage if more than two characters are in a scene.

There are many fine puppet books offering ideas if you like rod puppets. Please consult the Appendix for other books which might be of help to you.

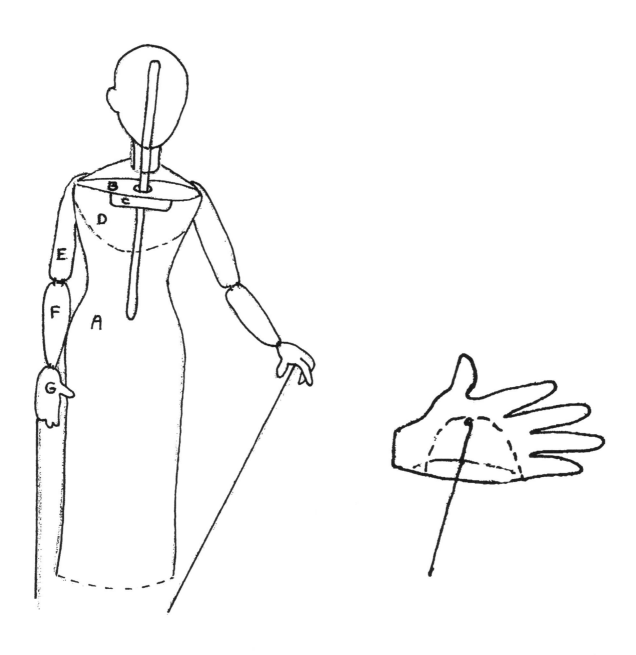

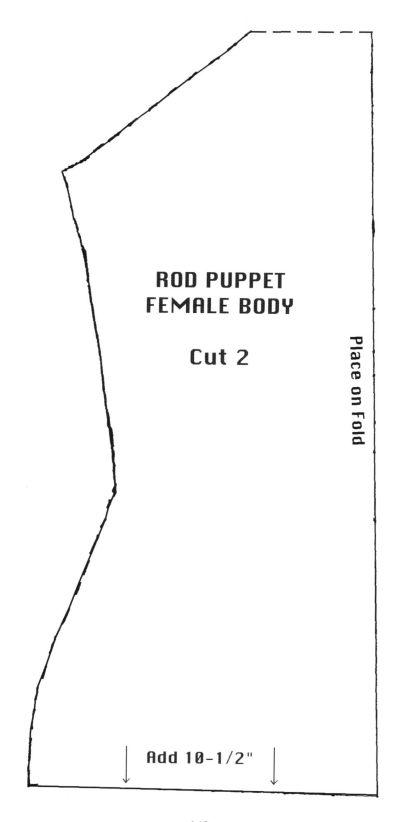

ROD PUPPET
FEMALE BODY

Cut 2

Place on Fold

Add 10-1/2"

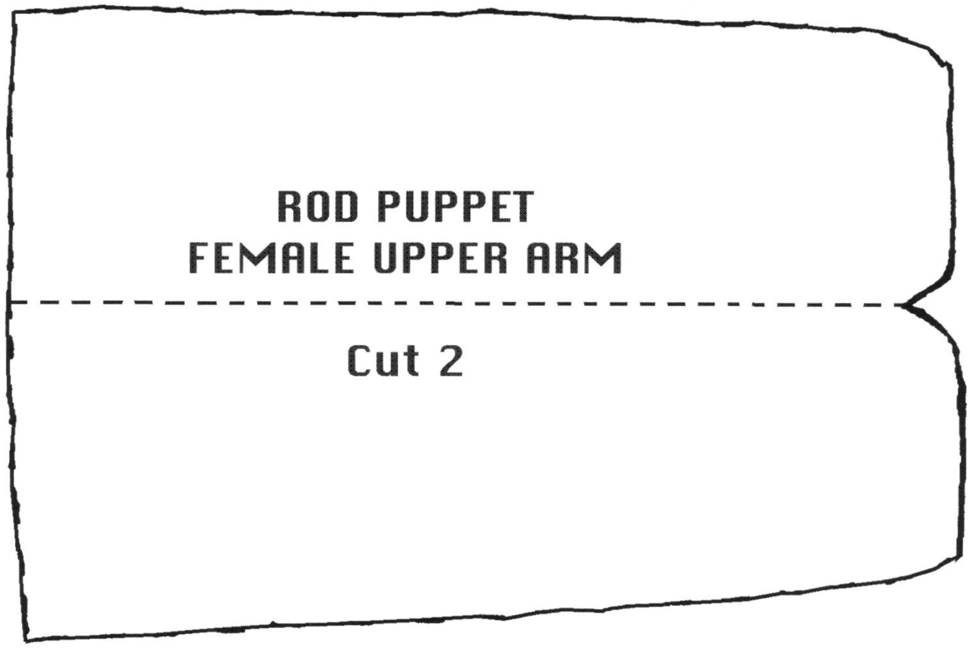

**ROD PUPPET
FEMALE UPPER ARM**

Cut 2

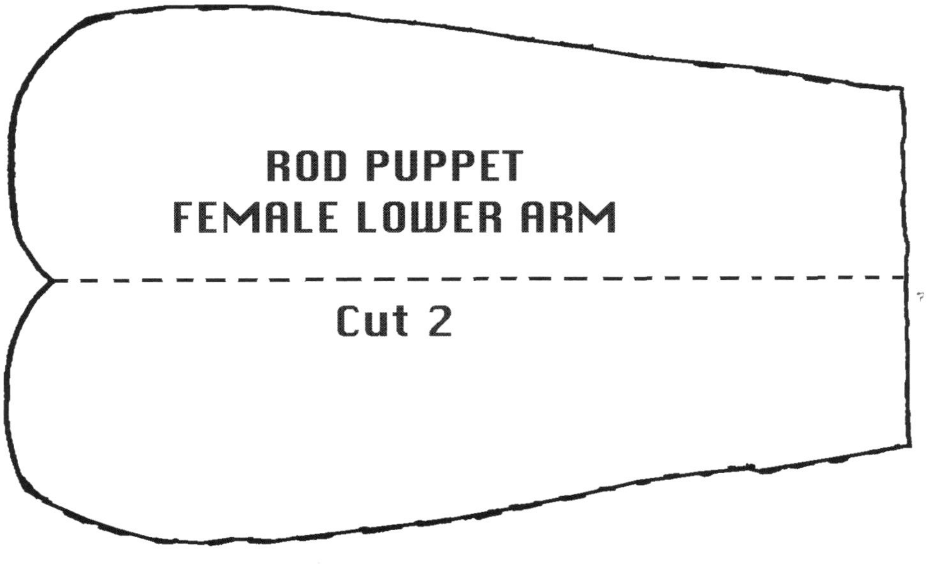

**ROD PUPPET
FEMALE LOWER ARM**

Cut 2

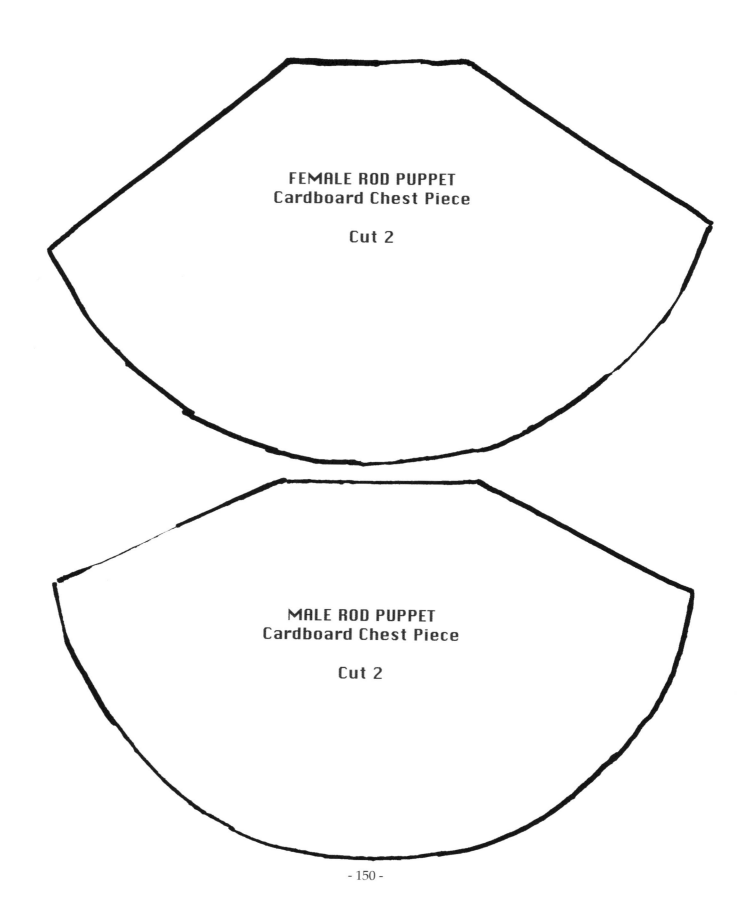

FEMALE ROD PUPPET
Cardboard Chest Piece

Cut 2

MALE ROD PUPPET
Cardboard Chest Piece

Cut 2

**ROD PUPPET
MALE BODY**

Cut 2

↓ Add 10-1/2" ↓

**ROD PUPPET
MALE UPPER ARM**

Cut 2

**ROD PUPPET
MALE LOWER ARM**

Cut 2

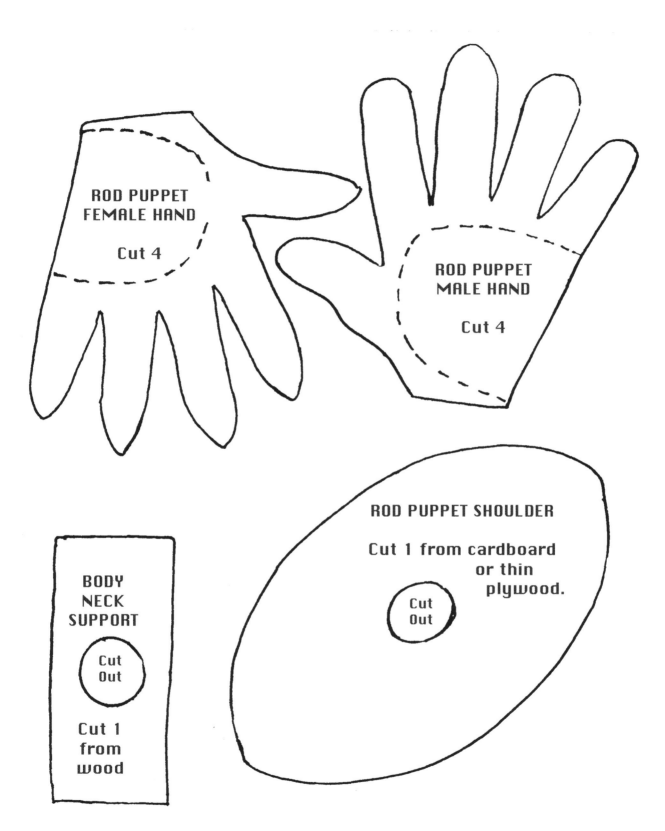

ROD PUPPET
FEMALE HAND

Cut 4

ROD PUPPET
MALE HAND

Cut 4

ROD PUPPET SHOULDER

Cut 1 from cardboard
or thin
plywood.

Cut
Out

BODY
NECK
SUPPORT

Cut
Out

Cut 1
from
wood

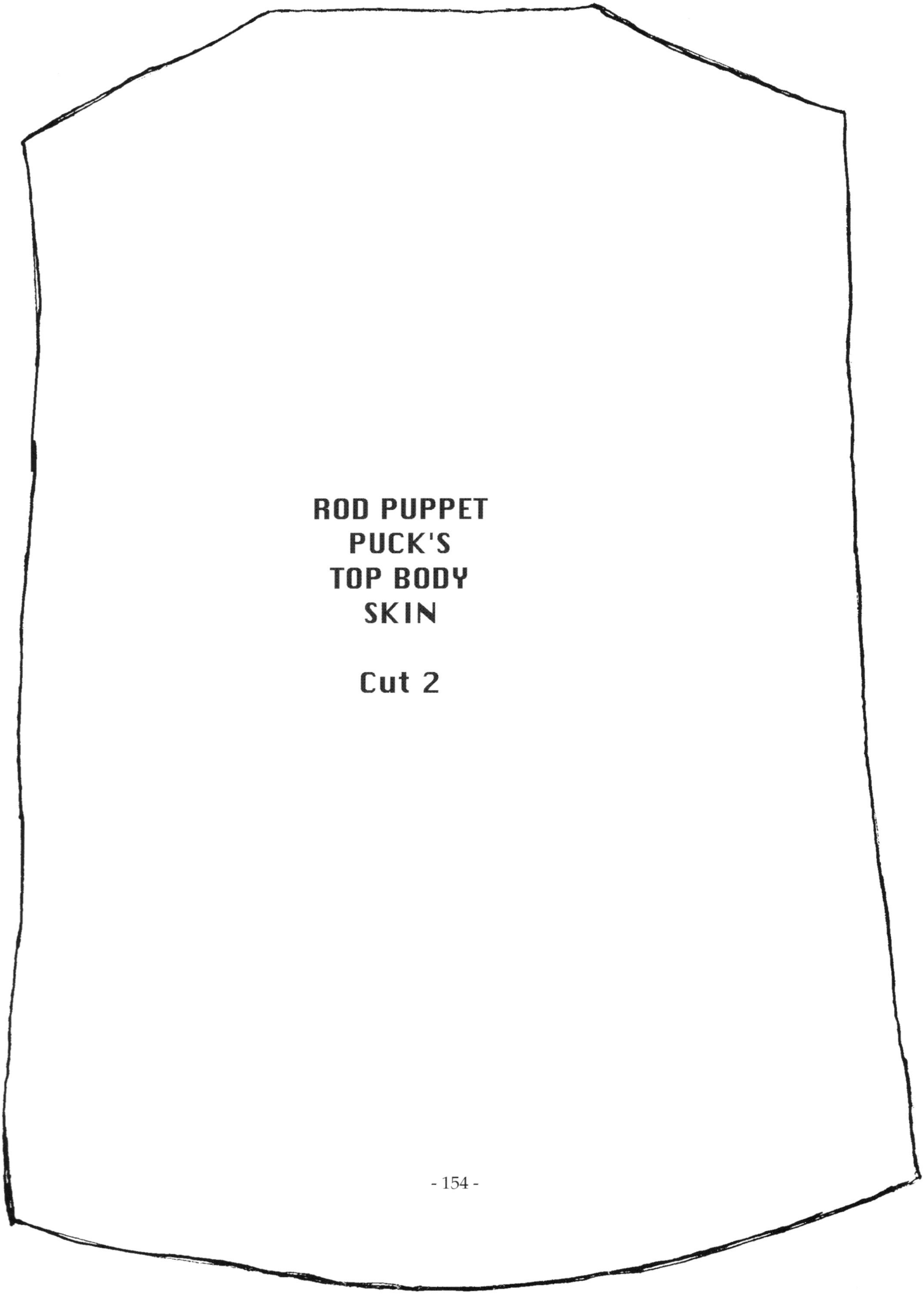

**ROD PUPPET
PUCK'S
TOP BODY
SKIN**

Cut 2

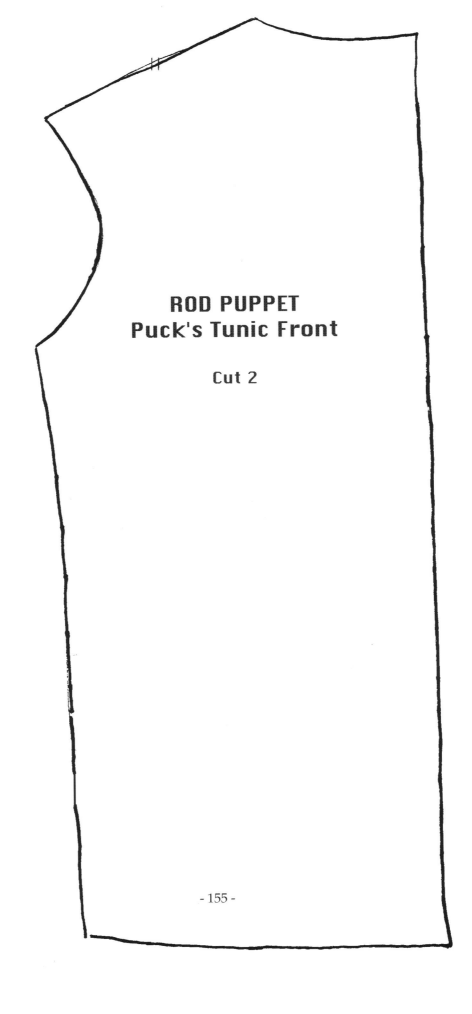

**ROD PUPPET
Puck's Tunic Front**

Cut 2

**ROD PUPPET
Puck's Tunic Back**

Cut 2

Fold

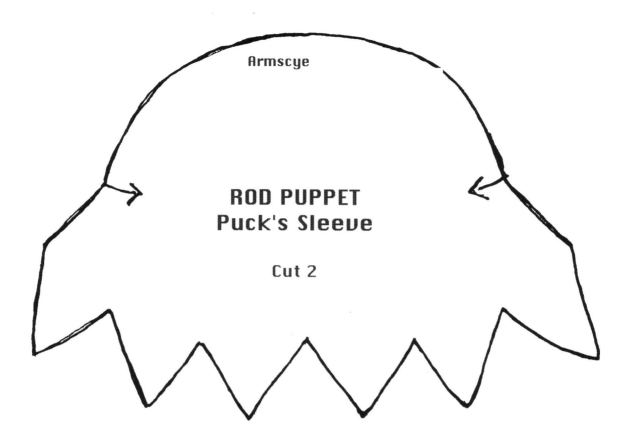

Armscye

**ROD PUPPET
Puck's Sleeve**

Cut 2

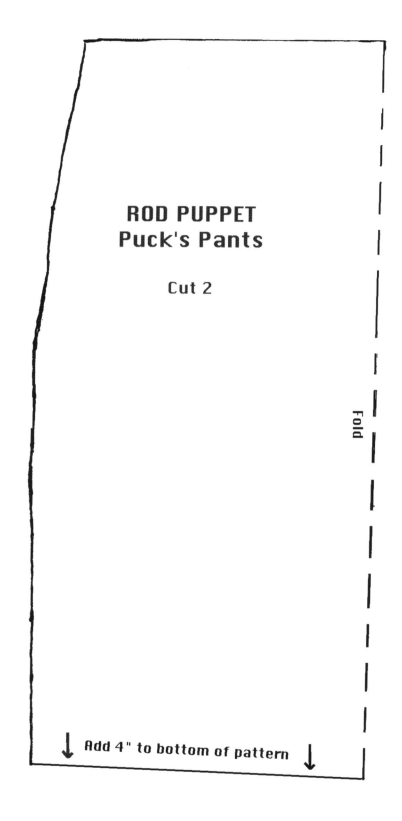

**ROD PUPPET
Puck's Pants**

Cut 2

Fold

↓ Add 4" to bottom of pattern ↓

CHAPTER 6: ADDING FINISHING TOUCHES

Our three puppet versions of Puck ready to perform. (Color photo on front cover.)

Just by using these basic patterns over and over again, an unlimited cast of puppet heroes, heroines or villains can be created.

Alas though, your training is far from complete. A good performer, puppeteer or artist is always learning and expanding on the skills. A fine puppeteer must also be a craftsman, artist, writer, musician, painter, carpenter, actor, dancer, and use many other sister skills. A wise mentor once told me it's very hard to be good at all of these. Focus on what you do best, and surround yourself with like friends and colleagues who pick up the slack. Great puppet theater can also be a great ensemble.

The art of puppetry is enjoying a theatrical renaissance today. More and more classical puppetry is being found on television, in schools and libraries, at public festivals and on the dramatic stage. Don't be afraid to find other puppeteers and combine visions to make a theatrical difference.

The careers of many of our fine puppeteers began in the early days with just such a book as the one you're holding.

Check your area for any nearby puppet guilds which you could join. Guilds are a good source of sharing ideas and keeping up with new innovations. Other good organizations to join are: the Puppeteers of America and UNIMA International. These large puppet groups hold yearly conferences and festivals, and publish knowledgeable newsletters and magazines.

I'd like to leave us with a few more nuggets of information, courtesy of Lewis Mahlmann who created most of these puppet patterns. They suggest other areas of puppet theater which you might look into. Again, check our Appendix for helpful books on these subjects.

On Producing A Puppet Show, Lewis Mahlmann suggests: (ideas reproduced from his books on puppet plays) *Plays For Young Puppeteers*, Boston: Plays Inc. 1993

> "*Simple Puppet Stages:*   *Every puppeteer needs a stage to perform his puppets on. There are many types you can make. The most common stage is one with a proscenium opening. This is where your puppet performs. There are many fine books with diagrams for making puppet stages. But if you want to make a quick puppet stage: fasten a blanket or sheet to a stick, and have two children hold the ends of the stick up; or put a tension curtain rod in the doorway and hang a curtain from it – use the open area above it for your proscenium opening!*
>
> *Props For The Puppet Stage:*   *Props and scenery can be as much fun to make as puppets themselves. Save boxes of many sizes to make such props as chairs, couches, thrones, chests, tables and cabinets. Doll toys make great small hand props. Shrubbery and trees can be cut from cardboard,*

painted and propped up on a stand. You can also make interesting greenery from crushed newspaper, and flowers from tissue or construction paper. Things found in nature also make great props and scenery!

<u>Scenery:</u> You can paint backdrops on brown wrapping paper, butcher paper, or muslin, but to simplify the stage design, use a set piece – a single piece of scenery such as a tree or house front cut out of cardboard, which leaves the rest of the stage free for any action. For example, a throne room would have just one large impressive throne - and a banner or two for color. A whole forest can be suggested with one large tree and a dark background or green cloth. Change the background to a light color and you have a garden. Even a fence with flowers on it tells the audience it is a friendly outdoor place. Perhaps your play may call for no scenery at all if it is short and the puppets are delightful to look at.

<u>Music In Puppetry:</u> Music is an important part of your puppet production. Whether you use live or recorded music, you should plan carefully to use some kind of musical accompaniment with your show. It creates the right atmosphere and bridges the gap between the scenes. It can be used to change the mood during acts, as background for action, and as rhythm for dances or pantomimes. Here are some reasons for using music:

1) Mood - to help bring out the emotional feeling or atmosphere of your play. Is it a happy play, a sad story, a fast-moving story, a silly play, or a serious one?

2) Bridges - the music you play while changing scenery. You mustn't let your audience grow restless while you change the scenery or when the action lags.

3) Songs or dances - try to find just the right dance or song accompaniment for the style of your show. Perhaps children's songs, new or old, might be just right for your story, even though you might have to change the lyrics to fit the action.

4) Background - Sometimes added music will enhance the action, as when the story is spooky or sad.
5) Opening overture - To get your show off to a good start!

You may use live music, if there is someone in your group who plays the piano, guitar, or recorder (or even simple instruments such as the mouth organ, or paper-over-comb). You may wish to add other instruments such as tambourines, rhythm sticks, bells or drums. Be original and create your own moods with sound!"

But above all, have fun - create - and don't let anyone tell you "It can't be done."

APPENDIX

A good library is a treasure which can never lose its worth!

If there's one thing I've learned over the years, it's to always count on my library to help figure out things I'd like to do. It used to be that good books on puppetry were hard to find. In this day of computers, an excellent puppet volume is just a click away.

To help build your own library, here are some of the best I've come across. Many of the titles listed can be found on the Puppeteers of America web site through their online store. Internet book sellers can help locate some of the older ones.

Puppet Making Books:

The following selections give a nice overview of creating the different types of puppets. Many include illustrations, diagraming puppet controls and methods. Puppet Stage ideas are also discussed in some of these.

Currell, David, *The Complete Book of Puppet Theater*. Barnes & Noble, Totowa, N.J., 1985.

Sinclair, Anita, *The Puppetry Handbook*. McPherson's Printing Group, Australia, 1995.

Wright, John, *Rod, Shadow and Glove, Puppets From The Little Angel Theater*. Robert Hale, London, 1986.

Marionette Books:

Here are some of my favorites books on making marionettes:

Abbe, Dorothy, *The Dwiggins Marionettes*. Harry N. Abrams, New York, 1969.

Baird, Bil, *The Art of the Puppet*. Macmillan, New York, 1965.

Beaton, Mabel and Les, *Marionettes, A Hobby for Everyone*. Dallas Puppet Theater Press, Dallas, 1989.

Coad, Luman, *The Marionette Source Book: Theory & Technique*. Charlemagne Press, Garden Bay, BC, 1993.

Fling, Helen, Marionettes: *How to Make and Work Them*. Dover, New York, 1973.

Fraser, Peter, *Puppets and Puppetry*, Peter Fraser. Stein & Day, New York, 1982.

Rod Puppet Books:

> Fettig, Hansjürgen, *Rod Puppets and Table-Top Puppets*. DaSilva Puppet Books, U.K. 1997. Out-of-print and very hard to find, but a treasure worth pursuing.

Shadow Puppet Books:

Shadow puppetry is another exciting variant of puppet. Through cut paper, light & shadow the puppets come alive. Shadow scenery can also be used behind dimensional puppets. Here are two good books on shadows.

> Currell, David, *Shadow Puppets & Shadow Play*. Crowood Press, U.K., 2007.

> Reiniger, Lotte, Shadow Puppets, *Shadow Theatres and Shadow Films*. Plays, Inc., Boston, 1975.

Books About Producing Puppet Plays:

Now that the puppets are made, here are some books with suggestions how the pros go about putting together a puppet show.

> Coad, Luman & Arlyn, *Producing For The Puppet Theatre*. Charlemagne Press, Garden Bay, BC, 1987.

> Cole, Nancy H., *Puppet Theatre in Performance*. William Morrow, New York, 1978.

> Latshaw, George, *Puppetry The Ultimate Disguise*. Richard Rosen, New York, 1978.

> Lee, Miles, *Puppet Theatre: Production and Manipulation*. Charlemagne Press, Garden Bay, BC, 1991.

> Magon, Jero, *Staging the Puppet Show*. Charlemagne Press, Garden Bay, BC, 1989.

Ten Eyck, Robert, *The Complete Book of Puppets and Puppeteering*. Drake Publishers, New York, 1976.

Books on Scenery & Props:

Here are a few non-puppet books describing how to make scenery and props. They are full of techniques, illustrations and wonderful zany ideas!

James, Thurston, *The Prop Builder's Molding & Casting Handbook*. Betterway, White Hall, VA, 1989.

James, Thurston, *The Theater Props Handbook*. Betterway, White Hall, VA, 1987.

Miller, James Hull, *Self-Supporting Scenery*. Meriwether, Colorado, 2006.

Biography Books on Puppeteers:

I can't express enough, how important it is to read biographies on puppeteers. Through experiencing their lives, you can become inspired to achieve greater successes. And it's always a good idea to see how others led the way in the exciting world of puppetry and theater. Here are a few of my favorites!

Brown, Forman, *Small Wonder: The Story of The Yale Puppeteers & Turnabout Theater*. Scarecrow Press, New Jersey, 1980.

Brown, Judy Barry and Luman Coad, *A Pair of Cockeyed Optimists: The Puppetry Career of Bob & Judy Brown*. Charlemagne Press, Garden Bay, BC, 2009.

Chessé Ralph, *The Marionette Actor*. George Mason University Press, Virginia, 1987.

Finch, Christopher, *Jim Henson: The Works, The Art, The Magic*. Random House, New York, 1993.

Grubidge, Dorlis, *Sue Hastings:Puppet Showwoman*. Charlemagne Press, Garden Bay, BC, 1993.

Hunt, Tamara Robin, *Tony Sarg: Puppeteer in America*. Charlemagne Press, Garden Bay, BC, 1988.

Lasky, Kathryn, *Puppeteer* (Paul Vincent Davis). Macmillan, New York, 1985.

Metz, Randal, Storybook Strings: *50 Years of Puppetry At Children's Fairyland's Storybook Puppet Theater*. Rappid Rabbit, Oakland, CA, 2003.

Randal Metz (author) has been a puppeteer since the age of 10. He has studied with Lewis Mahlmann, Bob Baker, Lettie Schubert, and completed a Master's Class taught by *The Muppets*. After twenty years as Artistic Director at Children's Fairyland, Randal moved across the lawn to become the director of Fairyland's Storybook Puppet Theater. He has a BA in Theater from San Francisco State University, has published two other books on Fairyland's rich history, and runs his own ***Puppet Company*** outside the park.

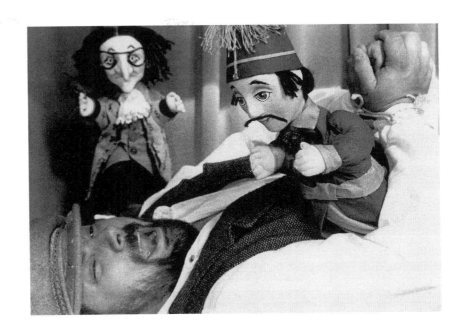

Carl LaRue (photographer) has held many jobs over the years. These include: mail room supervisor, head of a college learning resource center, photographer, police volunteer...... and puppeteer. While working at Fairyland, Carl became involved in the theater helping to build new shows. Carl has degrees in several fields, but enjoys being behind the lens of a camera these days. Several of his photos have been reproduced in local historical books.

Made in the USA
San Bernardino, CA
19 July 2014